This book belongs to

Mrs. M. K. Bayliss
1 Lansdowne Avenue
Portchester, Hants.
PO16 9NN Tel· 0705 384632

A·CELEBRATION·OF
FLOWERS

FRONTISPIECE
William Curtis. Oil painting attributed to Joseph Wright of Derby.

A·CELEBRATION·OF
FLOWERS

Two hundred years of Curtis's Botanical Magazine

RAY DESMOND

The Royal Botanic Gardens, Kew
in association with Collingridge

Published in 1987 by Collingridge Books
an imprint of The Hamlyn Publishing Group Limited
Bridge House, 69 London Road, Twickenham, Middlesex, England
in association with The Royal Botanic Gardens, Kew

ISBN 0 600 55075 3

Filmset in England by Vision Typesetting, Manchester
in 11 on $12\frac{1}{2}$pt. Baskerville

Printed in Spain

CONTENTS

COLOUR PLATES

PREFACE

I KNOW of no other illustrated botanical or horticultural periodical which has survived for as long as *Curtis's Botanical Magazine*; certainly no other publication resisted so resolutely modern photographic reproduction processes in favour of traditional hand-colouring for such a length of time. That the colouring of plates by hand was not abandoned until 1948 is a remarkable record.

The reputation of the Magazine has always resided in the accuracy of its portrayal of plants, originally copper engravings and then lithographs for many years. This pictorial record of garden and greenhouse plants from the temperate and tropical regions of the world has no rival. It is a chronicle of gardening taste over two centuries. Through its plates and associated text can be traced the progression of horticultural trends – the gradual ascendency, for instance, of orchids, rhododendrons and primulas. Some plants, once eagerly collected and assiduously cultivated, no longer enjoy their former popularity – begonias, ericas, calceolarias and pelargoniums (although in the case of begonias there is a revival of interest now that new species are being discovered in South East Asia). As different floristic regions were systematically explored, so there was a corresponding shift in the interest of gardeners and botanists. For several centuries the hardy trees and shrubs of North America made the greatest impact on British gardens; in turn South Africa, Australia, Central and South America, and China came to the fore as plant collectors harvested their floral treasures. Much of this fluctuation in fashion can be gleaned from the *Botanical Magazine* whose editors have consistently chosen plants of horticultural or botanical distinction to figure in its volumes. Editors such as Sir Joseph Hooker were refreshingly outspoken in condemning what they considered to be undesirable practices – carpet bedding, for example. I have quoted liberally from such editorial comment in order to emphasize the point that the plates should not be allowed to overshadow the value of the text as a reflection of contemporary opinion.

Nevertheless, it is this unique gallery of plant portraits, in over 180 volumes, which has made the *Botanical Magazine* world-famous. The hundred or so artists who drew for the Magazine are all listed in the Appendix, and, for the first time, it is now possible to find their contributions among the 10,000 plates with relative ease.

This is the story of a periodical which has endured many crises – conflicts between proprietors, editors and artists, as well as financial difficulties. But every time it hovered on the brink of closure, there was always an individual or a group of people who came to its support. Through its long history, the *Botanical*

Magazine has had its critics but it has never lacked friends: its loyal band of subscribers; nurserymen and gardeners who sent it their choice blooms; botanists who identified them and wrote authoritative descriptions; and, in the distant colonies, governors, consuls, curators of botanical gardens, and merchants who sent plants to Kew.

This account begins, quite properly, with an assessment of the aims and achievements of the Magazine's founder, William Curtis, a man of vision and purpose. His creation has outlived all its competitors who sought to emulate it, some even copying its plates. Curtis's ideals and goals are preserved in the *Kew Magazine* which, although extending its editorial horizons, maintains the traditions of accuracy and quality which made the *Botanical Magazine* an instant success when it was launched in 1787.

1

THE FOUNDER

WILLIAM Curtis, the founder of *Curtis's Botanical Magazine*, grew up in Alton in Hampshire, a small town straggling the London road in a gentle valley between chalk hills. He was born on January 11, 1746 in an early eighteenth-century house – now called Brooklands – in Lenton Street. His father, John Curtis, was a tanner and a Quaker (the Society of Friends had established themselves in the town in the late seventeenth century when William Curtis's great grandfather, Thomas Curtis, a physician and maltster, had joined them). It is believed that William Curtis attended a Friends' school at Burford in Oxfordshire.

Even as a schoolboy William Curtis showed signs of a compulsive interest in natural history that was to dominate his adult life. Since his grandfather, John Curtis, a surgeon-apothecary in the town, had agreed to accept William as an apprentice on leaving school, his father did nothing to discourage an inclination which would be useful in his medical studies. Adjacent to John Curtis's surgery was the Crown Inn where William made friends with the ostler, Thomas Legg, whose intimacy with the local flora was founded on the classic herbals of Gerard and Parkinson. Legg became his mentor and William happily spent all his pocket money on natural history books. Fearing the boy was devoting far too much time to natural history, his grandfather transferred his apprenticeship to a fellow apothecary, George Vaux, in the City of London. Not long afterwards William entered the employ of another London apothecary, Thomas Talwin of 51 Gracechurch Street. He studied anatomy at St Thomas's Hospital and assisted the senior physician, George Fordyce, in practical botanical demonstrations.

On Talwin's death William, now a qualified apothecary, purchased his former employer's prosperous practice, but he had no inclination whatever for the profession. A partnership with William Wavell about 1770 gave him more spare time for his natural history pursuits, but his discontent persisted. While still in his mid-twenties, he took a bold step of selling his share of the practice to Wavell but went on living and practising medicine at Gracechurch Street for some years.[1] As his contemporary, Sir James Edward Smith, commented: 'The street-walking duties of a city practitioner but ill accorded with the wild excursions of a naturalist: the apothecary was soon swallowed up in the botanist, and the shop exchanged for a garden.'[2]

Some of his friends including the brothers of the Rev. Gilbert White of Selborne, Thomas and Benjamin, supported him in a venture to create a garden

[1] A plaque records the site of the house.
[2] A. Rees, *The cyclopaedia*, vol. 10, 1819.

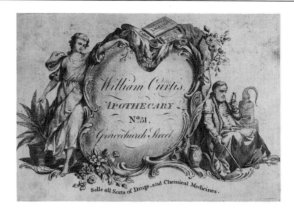

William Curtis's trade card.

of British plants. In 1771, he acquired about an acre of land in Spring or Restoration Garden in Lambeth.[3]

The same year saw the publication of his first book, a slim pamphlet of 24 pages, *Instructions for collecting and preserving insects, particularly moths and butterflies* (price 1s.). It has one unsigned folded plate, engraved by T. Fougeron, depicting apparatus and methods for pinning and setting insects. Joseph Banks, recently returned to England from Captain Cook's voyage on the *Endeavour*, politely acknowledged a presentation copy, adding encouragingly that it was 'a work which has long been wanted and cannot but be useful to the science of Natural History especially in increasing the number of entomologists'.

In 1772 there appeared yet another entomological work by Curtis, *Fundamenta entomologiae: or, an introduction to the knowledge of insects. Being a translation of the Fundamenta entomologiae of Linnaeus*. Like the earlier work, it was sold by G. Pearce of Cheapside but was a much more ambitious effort with 90 pages of text and two engraved plates.

William Curtis was gradually and quietly establishing a modest reputation as a naturalist. His friend, Stanesby Alchorne, assay-master in the Mint, who had temporarily been Demonstrator of Botany at the Chelsea Physic Garden since 1771, recommended Curtis to succeed him.

The Chelsea Physic Garden had been formed on a 1.5 ha (3.5 acre) site on the banks of the Thames by the Worshipful Society of Apothecaries of London in 1673. In 1714 the Society sought financial assistance to maintain the garden from Sir Hans Sloane who, having purchased the Manor of Chelsea, was the owner of the Garden's freehold. Sloane who had known the Garden as a medical student, and now a man of considerable wealth and a keen naturalist, was sympathetic to their approach. In 1722 he arranged a new lease at £5 a year in perpetuity to preserve the Garden's future but only 'on condition that it be for ever kept up and maintain'd by the Company as a Physick Garden'. To ensure the observance of this requirement the Society was to deliver every year 50

[3] G. Gibberd, 'The location of William Curtis's London Botanic Garden in Lambeth' (*Garden History*, vol. 13, no. 1, 1985, pp. 9–16).

plants from its Garden to the Royal Society until 2,000 pressed and mounted specimens had been accumulated. At the same time Sloane was also directly responsible for the appointment of Philip Miller to manage the Garden. During the 50 years he held the post, he made the Garden an important centre for new and rare plants from abroad. When the distinguished Swedish naturalist, Linnaeus, visited England in 1736, the Physic Garden at Chelsea was one of the places he wanted to see. Probably the most influential horticultural publication of the eighteenth century was Miller's *Gardener's dictionary* (1731) which went through eight editions (eighth edition, 1768). William Forsyth followed Miller in 1770 as Gardener. When the Society of Apothecaries was notified in December 1771 by Alchorne of his intention to resign as Demonstrator of Botany, a successor was sought. A year later, William Curtis who had applied for the post was appointed to start in 1773, at an annual salary of £30.

Having made this new appointment, it was an opportunity for the Society to re-examine and redefine the duties of the 'office of Botanick Demonstrator'. The incumbent was to supervise the running of the Garden and the library; to be present 'not less than once every Summer Month (i.e. from April to September both inclusive) to demonstrate the Plants, especially in the official Quarter with their names and uses. . . . He is expected to make some annual Excursion for two Days at least preparatory to the Society's General Herborizing; inviting two or three of the ablest botanical Members to his Assistance. The instruction being to collect such Vegitables [sic] as are not commonly found in the environs of the Metropolis, to be demonstrated by him at the meeting appointed for that purpose. . . . He is to accompany and conduct the Students of this Society in their search after indigenous Plants upon every day appointed for their private Herborizings: (which are only 5 in each Summer;) when he is desired to use his best endeavour for preserving strict decorum among his Pupils: and for directing and confining their attention solely to the intended business of the day – and, as the regular Lectures on these occasions at the request of the Master & Wardens, have on account of the times and places appeared insufficient for teaching accurately the Elements of the botanic Science it is now recommended for the Demonstrator to consider of some more effectual Methods for answering so desirable an end. . . . Moreover, He is yearly to prepare fifty dryed specimens from Plants growing in the Society's Garden at Chelsea, which are to be presented to the Royal Society, by the direction of the late Sᴿ Hans Sloane Baronet having been first approved by the Court of Assistants of this Society'. The Demonstrator was also to be present at the monthly meetings of the Private Court during the Summer and to be Secretary of the General Committee for Managing the Garden and 'to cultivate an extensive botanical correspondence both at home and abroad'.[4] With this comprehensive definition of the duties of the Demonstrator, one wonders what was left for William Forsyth to do!

At a General Meeting on April 16, 1773 William Curtis was confirmed in his appointment as the Society's Demonstrator and 'acknowledged himself well satisfied with the rules prescribed for his conduct; and promised to use his best

[4] Guildhall Library. Chelsea Physic Garden Order Book 1771–1829. MS 8236, March 21, 1773.

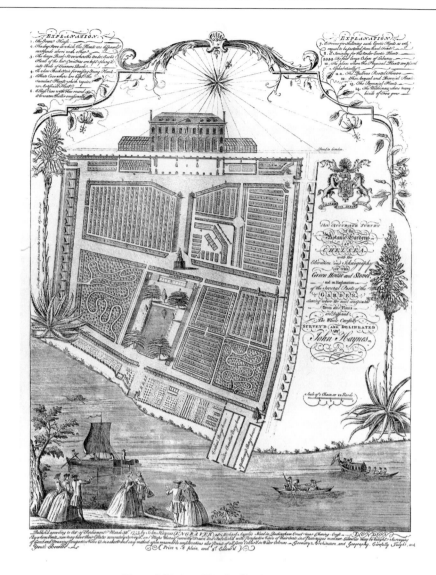

Plan of Chelsea Physic Garden, 1753.

endeavours for promoting the Science of Botany, and the Society's Honour'.

One of Curtis's first projects at Chelsea was the incorporation of 'a large quantity of lava, brought from the Volcano on Iceland' by Joseph Banks to create a rock-garden 'for the cultivation of such plants as will only thrive in Stoney soils'. At the Committee meeting in August Curtis reported the completion of the rockery, and his proposal to expand Linnaeus's *Principia botanica* in a series of student lectures was approved.

These harmonious relations were not destined to last for long. The first note of discord appears in the Minutes of the Court of Assistants for August 16, 1774 which record that Curtis had failed to give his lectures at the Physic Garden. In

October 1776 the Court rejected his request 'to take into Partnership a person not of the Society to assist him in his business as an apothecary' although if this were sanctioned he promised to be more punctual in his attendance at the Garden. He again incurred their displeasure by neglecting to attend a Court Meeting in April 1777. More serious was his failure to deliver the annual donation of 50 plants to the Royal Society as required under the terms of Sir Hans Sloane's lease. Several times he broke his promise to despatch these plants. He informed a Meeting of the Court on August 27, 1777 that he had at last delivered the plants and attributed his negligence to 'Business and therefore desired leave to resign his place'. The Minutes tersely record that 'the Court informed the said Mr Curtis that they were very much disatisfied with his conduct and therefore accepted his resignation' and ordered that he presented at 'the next private Court the several setts of Plants which he ought to have delivered to the Royal Society, in the years 1774, 1775 and 1776 respectively'.[5]

His preoccupation with the preparation and publication of the ambitiously conceived *Flora Londinensis* was the most likely cause for the neglect of his duties at Chelsea. Even a man of his considerable energy and drive could not sustain this dual role to everyone's satisfaction. On August 28, 1777 Sir Thomas Frankland wrote from Yorkshire to Joseph Banks informing him that he had 'received a letter from Curtis, stating that he proposes to give up his business as an apothecary and give himself up entirely to his garden & *Flora*. To enable him to do this he says he shall be obliged to request the loan of £50 for a year from a few of his Friends. I have no doubt that this will be agreeable news to you, as one need not doubt seeing the work go on with spirit'.[6] In a subsequent letter Frankland is less sympathetic, wondering why Curtis needed 'to raise a sum on quitting his profession. He has not hitherto been obliged to borrow money to forward his work, and owns that it has had a most favourable sale: He appears therefore to have capital enough to carry it on, particularly if he sells his stock in trade'.[7]

Sumptuously illustrated and extravagantly contrived flower books like the *Flora Londinensis*, now so admired and avidly sought by collectors, were largely the product of the closing years of the eighteenth century and the opening decades of the nineteenth. In 1815 Goethe was mildly astonished by 'the mad luxury carried on in England with regard to books'. National pride had something to do with these grand gestures in book-making. R. J. Thornton (who wrote the first lengthy biographical account of William Curtis)[8] was convinced that in publishing his impressive *Temple of Flora*, he was engaged upon 'a national undertaking'. Subscribers were the sole support of most of these elegant productions. Curtis found to his cost that although he had recruited 318 subscribers the number was insufficient to see his *Flora Londinensis* through to its planned conclusion.

According to an approving Thornton, he had 'conceived the sublime notion

---

[5] Guildhall Library. Society of Apothecaries. Court of Assistants Minutes. MS 8201/12.
[6] Royal Botanic Gardens, Kew. Library (Archives). Sir Joseph Banks letters, vol. 1, item 63.
[7] *Ibid*, item 65, November 14, 1777.
[8] W. Curtis, *Lectures on Botany*, 1805, vol. 3.

of giving *A complete Natural History of the British Isles with Plates of each Object*, not upon a neat, diminutive, inadequate scale, but one that was equally just, magnificent, and noble, like our Empire – one truly worthy of the British Nation'.[9] Thornton mentions several hundred drawings of birds and animals, mostly the work of Sydenham Edwards, which were intended for Curtis's grand design, a 'History of the Natural Productions of Great Britain'.[10] But, declared Thornton, 'the attempt was as new as it was grand; and, fearful of the disgrace of not succeeding in so extensive and hazardous an enterprise, he sounded first the public mind, by publishing proposals for a *part* of this great national work, which he should have entitled Flora Anglica, or Flora Britannica, but which he called "Flora Londinensis"'.[11] In this ambitious endeavour Curtis was encouraged by the Kent antiquary and botanist, William Boys. 'I cannot restrain myself from telling you how much you have obliged and pleased me with your first number of the Flora Londinensis and the notice you give of proceeding to publish not only the London plants but with proper encouragement all the indigenous plants of Great Britain. Go on securely! The singular merit of the work I confidently augur, will ensure you pleasure, reputation and success'.[12]

The *Flora Londinensis* was confined to plants growing within ten miles of London but had the work prospered, Curtis had every intention of covering the rest of the country. The plant portraits in this folio work were drawn life-size and in the case of very large plants only a part could be depicted. The paper was purchased from some of the best English papermakers and Curtis employed the ablest artists and engravers he could afford. Very slowly 72 parts were published between 1775 and 1798, each with six plates. An uncoloured part cost 2s.6d., 5s. if it were coloured, and 7s.6d. if extra special care had been bestowed on the hand-colouring.

Most of the plates are unsigned but the first of the two volumes is largely the work of William Kilburn. He had been a designer for London calico printers and print shops when Curtis engaged him to draw and engrave the plates for the *Flora*. Sir James Edward Smith made the interesting comment that Kilburn used a camera obscura to draw the plants.[13] When Kilburn returned to the more profitable calico printing some time between 1777 and 1778 he was replaced by James Sowerby and Sydenham Edwards as artist and engraver. Some of the plates were engraved by Thomas Milton, F. Sansom and W. Darton.

The hand-colouring of the copper-engraved plates was done under the supervision of William Graves, a specialist in natural history works. Samuel Curtis, William Curtis's son-in-law, recorded that Graves worked for Curtis from 1771, colouring all his publications. With a team of colourists, the hand-colouring was inevitably uneven in quality. William Hird of Leeds complained that 'the colouring of every plant in the first number in my possession is by no means equal to the specimen Cousin Nancy Freeman left with me'.[14] He was,

[9] W. Curtis, *Lectures on Botany*, 1805, vol 3, p. 16.
[10] *Ibid*, p. 29.
[11] *Ibid*, pp. 16–17.
[12] W. H. Curtis, *William Curtis, 1746–1799*, 1941, p. 20, May 21, 1775.
[13] A. Rees, *The cyclopaedia*, vol. 10, 1819.
[14] Curtis Museum, Alton. Curtis letters, item 20, June 13, 1775.

PLATE I
William Curtis. Watercolour miniature by Peter Paillou, 1798. Peter Paillou is
probably better known as a zoological artist.

however, content with a 7s.6d. number, extra carefully coloured (perhaps by William Graves himself). Curtis must have dreaded every letter from Sir Thomas Frankland, always pernickety and seldom satisfied. The colouring was a constant irritant. '*Veronica officinalis* very good except the colouring of the flowers which is, contrary to the rule I should follow, done with opaque colours. I have not seen a single instance of opaque colours throughout your whole work without this spoiling the flowers – I had far rather have no colour at all'.[15] Frankland monotonously laments the departure of Kilburn. 'I heartily wish Kilburn would execute some of the orchis's for you next Spring. There is an uncommon taste in his drawing & I often regret that he has deserted you'.[16] Nor did the quality of the engraving escape his fastidious eye. 'The principal merit of the plates still lies in the *draughtsman*, as the engraving is in many instances bad'.[17] His litany of complaints never eases up. 'There is a harshness in the engraving of many latter plates which is not to be got over, and makes one cry out for Kilburn and Sansom'.[18] Sansom's successor (W. Darton?) had 'neither delicacy or freedom in any of his strokes'.[19]

Of much greater concern to most subscribers was the irregular and infrequent publication of successive numbers of the *Flora*. T. J. Woodward was convinced that 'there is not the most distant possibility of Mr Curtis's ever publishing all the plants in Gt. Britain. At the rate he has lately gone on it would take three centuries for that purpose'. The Rev. John Lightfoot tried to shame him into 'a more speedy Progress in the Work. . . . I thought you a Man of more Spirit & Perseverance than to creep at the Rate of a Number in two Months. Let me entreat you for the Sake of your own Credit & Reputation, for the Sake of your own Interest to move on with more Vigour and Expedition'.[20] In the preface to the first volume (1777) Curtis made the loss of Kilburn an excuse for delay but confidently predicted that his replacement by two other artists – Sowerby and Edwards – would ensure regular publication in the future, a promise that was never kept.

A serious shortcoming for any user of the *Flora* is the absence of consecutive numbers on the plates, a defect which prompted the Rev. Lightfoot to admonish Curtis. 'I was never more embarrassed in my life than when I set about quoting your Figures in the Appendix of the Flor: Scotica.[21] . . . How absurd then must it appear when no Authors know how to *cite* you; and if they should, no two of them will probably agree. . . . Let me entreat you to figure your *future* Numbers & *we* will page your past Numbers'.[22] Curtis had intended the plates to be rearranged by subscribers according to Linnaeus's classification of plants.

The severe financial burden of the *Flora* compelled Curtis to appeal for a loan

[15] Curtis Museum, Alton. Curtis letters, item 116, February 16, 1781.
[16] *Ibid*, item 71–72, December 21, 1778.
[17] *Ibid*, item 156, January 13, 1782.
[18] *Ibid*, item 193–94, May 20, 1783.
[19] *Ibid*, item 175, August 15, 1781.
[20] *Ibid*, item 136–37, August 28, 1781.
[21] J. Lightfoot, *Flora Scotica*, 1777, 2 volumes.
[22] Curtis Museum, Alton. Curtis letters, item 51–52, December 22, 1777.

to Lord Bute, former adviser to Princess Augusta on the creation of her garden at Kew and a very able amateur botanist. The Hon. Daines Barrington, replying on behalf of Lord Bute, indicated that 'Lord Bute is willing to contribute munificently without any expectation of interest or return of capital to the expediting of your publication. . . . Under the circumstances I should advise you to dedicate your work to Lord Bute as you propose & I have no doubt but that he will shew himself to be a real protector to the study of botany'.[23] Volume one was duly dedicated to Lord Bute by its extremely grateful author.

Another monetary crisis sent Curtis to his friend Dr John Coakley Lettsom, a fellow Quaker, whose garden at Grove Hill, Camberwell was one of Lettsom's greatest joys. He generously sent Curtis £500 in instalments with evidently little intention of reclaiming the debt. 'As to my acct. I have paid no attention to it lately, nor shall I ever demand it, unless thou wishes to discharge it. Keep this [letter] therefore as a security against any demand that I or my survivors may make. I am rather disposed to serve thee further, would that assist thee in the prosecution of thy work, which I consider as a National honour'.[24] Curtis accordingly dedicated the second volume (1798) to Lettsom, 'the patron of science'.

In 1790 James Sowerby, one of the artists of the *Flora Londinensis*, launched the first number of his *English Botany* for which he drew and engraved the plates himself. Curtis unreasonably viewed the new publication 'as an act of hostility against himself',[25] especially as the format was remarkably like his *Botanical Magazine*, even to the same blue wrappers. J. E. Smith who wrote the text for Sowerby attempted in vain to placate Curtis: 'if he thought the book likely at all to interfere with the success of his *Flora*, we should confine it to such plants as were not to be found within ten miles of London'.[26] Curtis rejected both the offer and his former friend and retaliated with *An abridgement of the Flora Londinensis with reduced plates*. The plant figures were redrawn and reduced two-fifths but after six parts (1792–93), with 36 plain plates by Sansom, the work was discontinued.

In an effort to shake his friend out of one of his depressions, Dr Goodenough assured Curtis that the *Flora Londinensis* was '*your glory*, your *best friend*, your everything'.[27] Curtis had tried desperately to keep the project going: the legacy from his father, the income from his lectures, the subscriptions from his Lambeth garden, donations and loans from friends – all had been used to finance his *Flora* but to no avail. It came to a premature end in 1798 through a lack of support occasioned, so Dr Goodenough thought, by unacceptable tardiness in publication.[28] Samuel Curtis, much more of a shrewd businessman, firmly believed that his father-in-law should have priced it more realistically from the start, 'whereas it was published so near its actual cost, as, with the outlay upon the

[23] *Ibid*, item 120–21, March 26, 1781.
[24] *Ibid*, item 212, February 4, 1784.
[25] S. Goodenough, *Gentleman's Magazine*, August 1799, p. 637.
[26] J. Sowerby, *English Botany*, vol. 7, 1798, preface, p. ii.
[27] Curtis Museum, Alton. Curtis letters, item 290, January 8, 1791.
[28] *Gentleman's Magazine*, August 1799, pp. 636–37.

PLATE 2
Samuel Curtis. Watercolour miniature.

stocks remaining on hand, involved the author in difficulties'.[29]

The scrupulous accuracy of its drawings places it among the finest of illustrated English floras. Sir Joseph Banks recommended its plates to the East India Company as a model for their proposed *Plants of the coast of Coromandel*. Sir James Edward Smith, President of the Linnean Society, asserted that 'independent of its excellent figures, [it] ranks next to Ray's *Synopsis* in original merit and authority upon English plants'.[30] The Professor of Botany at Edinburgh, John Hope, was confident that 'it certainly will while science remains be an honourable & lasting Monument of the Great obligations Botany owes you'.[31]

William Curtis's will bequeathed his entire estate, including the *Flora Londinensis*, to his wife Mary and his daughter Sarah. In 1801 Sarah married her father's cousin, Samuel Curtis, who the following year paid £600 to the executors of William Curtis's estate for the purchase of the *Flora* and miscellaneous plates. In 1815, having done nothing with his acquisition, Samuel Curtis sold the copyright and some copper plates of insects and birds[32] to George Graves (1784–*c*.1839), son of the colourer, William Graves. George Graves, intent on publishing a new edition, engaged William Jackson Hooker, Professor of Botany at Glasgow University, as collaborator. It came out in five volumes between 1817 and 1828, the first three volumes reprinting the copper plates of the original work; volumes four and five for which Hooker provided the descriptions were illustrated by Hooker and R. K. Greville, and engraved by J. Swan of Glasgow. (It is interesting to note the presence of a solitary lithograph amongst all the engraved plates, that of *Boletus sulphureus*.) The original work had confined itself, with a few exceptions, to the flora of the environs of London; the title page of the second edition extended it to 'the plants indigenous to Great Britain'. The disappointing response from the public Sir Joseph Hooker attributed to the 'incredible mismanagement' of George Graves; 'this rare and beautiful work', wrote Sir Joseph, 'was produced at great cost under financial embarrassment of the Editor (Mr Graves) and its end is probably unique in the history of botanical works – Chancery!'.[33]

On June 4, 1834 an agreement was drawn up between the four purchasers of the work: 'Mr Graves having reported that Mr Dowding had gone from his first offer, & declined to give more than £100 above the value of Waste Paper & Old Copper for the *Flora Londinensis* & that only on condition of 5 copies being completed for him by us which would cost about £30 – It was proposed to Mr

[29] S. Curtis, 'Memoir of the life and writings of the late Mr. William Curtis', 1828, p. xii.
[30] *Transactions of the Linnean Society*, vol. 4, 1798, p. 280.
[31] Curtis Museum, Alton. Curtis Letters, item 124, April 7, 1781.
[32] According to Samuel Curtis, George Graves subsequently published the bird plates, i.e. in his *British ornithology*, 1811, ('Memoir of the life and writings of the late Mr. William Curtis', p. xxix). There exists in the Linnean Society a manuscript lecture by William Curtis written on the back of cut-up engravings of birds. These fragments, probably proof copies, carry the imprint 'Published by W. Curtis Feby 1 1785'. Sydenham Edwards was the artist. Another fragment of a bird plate is in the Curtis Museum at Alton (W. H. Curtis, *William Curtis*, p. 21).
[33] *Annals of Botany*, vol. 16, 1902, p. xcix.

William Curtis's London Botanic Garden at Lambeth.
Watercolour by James Sowerby.

Graves that the entire Work, in the state in which it is now, should be *his* upon his paying us the sum of £226 for it – the £200 in approved bills . . . and £26 to be set against the same amount here to him for colouring'.[34] The work was the ruin of George Graves. The only person to benefit was the ever alert publisher of remaindered books, Henry G. Bohn of Covent Garden. He purchased everything from the modest manual to the fine folio, not even disdaining loose plates. He re-issued the *Flora Londinensis* in 1835 with slightly different title pages; in 1847 he still had a few copies available at £30 (the original price had been £87 4s.) – 'as the present reduced price scarcely repays the cost of colouring, there is no probability that the work will ever be reprinted'.[35]

During the stressful years William Curtis was supervising and promoting the publication of the *Flora Londinensis*, he did not neglect the acre site in Lambeth situated near the present Old Vic Theatre[36] which he had purchased in 1771. In 1778 he distributed *Proposals for opening by subscription a botanic garden to be called the London Botanic Garden* prior to opening in January the following year. Through the generous presentation of plants from the royal garden at Kew, Chelsea Physic Garden, Lord Bute and many of his friends he was able to cultivate and display a reasonable nucleus of British and foreign plants. They were all clearly labelled with their Linnean names supplemented by a colour code indicating their use in medicine, agriculture, etc. In due course a catalogue was published. The *Catalogue of the British medicinal, culinary and agricultural plants cultivated in the London Botanic Garden* (1783) listed the names of 40 subscribers who, for an annual subscription of one guinea, were entitled to bring a friend when they

[34] St Bride's Printing Library. Taylor & Francis papers.
[35] H. G. Bohn, *Catalogue*, 1847, p. 32.
[36] G. Gibberd 'The location of William Curtis's London Botanic Garden in Lambeth' (*Garden History*, vol. 13, no. 1, 1985, pp. 9–16).

visited the Garden; a two guinea subscription offered the additional benefit of acquiring plants and seeds. A library of just over 100 titles was also open to subscribers. Curtis also delivered a series of public lectures at the Garden and subsequently published them as *A companion to the Botanical Magazine*.[37]

After 18 years at Lambeth Marsh, industrial pollution and unfavourable terms for the renewal of the lease of the Garden compelled Curtis to move in 1789. He found a site in West London at Brompton, a traditional centre for nurseries and market gardens. The Brompton Botanic Garden,[38] as it was called, was open daily from six o'clock in the morning to eight in the evening, April to September, and from eight to four o'clock for the rest of the year. Subscriptions remained at one and two guineas; in 1801 there were 213 subscribers; non-subscribers were charged 2s.6d. a visit. Catalogues of the plants appear to have been published for most years of the Garden's existence. The main collection occupied 1.5 ha (3.5 acres) and an adjacent plot of 3 ha (7 acres) was devoted to experimental agriculture. Subscribers could no longer borrow books from the library which had now grown to some 250 titles; it seems that a large collection of natural history drawings was also available for consultation. When a German visitor inspected the Garden only a few months after Curtis's death he thought it 'very pretty and well-cared for'.[39]

When Adrian Hardy Haworth left Yorkshire in 1792 to live in Chelsea, he promptly became one of the Garden's subscribers and through a mutual interest in botany and entomology soon became friendly with Curtis. His home in Salamanca Place housed a collection of about 40,000 insects, a herbarium of about 20,000 plants, a shell collection and a library of 1,600 volumes on natural history. He was the foremost authority on succulent plants and complimented Curtis on his collection of mesembryanthemums. Curtis was one of the sponsors for his Fellowship of the Linnean Society. Some years later Haworth recalled that 'on my mentioning to Mr Curtis, some time before his death my intention of attempting the establishment of a society to collect and explain all the natural productions of Great Britain, or, at the very least, entomological ones, he assured me that he had once meditated a similar thing himself, under the appellation of *Musaeolum Britannicum*; and as he had abandoned the idea of pursuing it, he presented me with his *Collection of British insects*, to engage me to do so'.[40] This generous gesture is confirmation of the respect and regard that Curtis had for his young friend and an undated Memorandum reveals that Curtis saw him as a possible partner. 'If a lease of 21 years can be procured, and a small Bark Stove & Museum be constructed, after a plan proposed below, Mr Haworth is agreeable

[37] *A companion to the Botanical Magazine; or, a familiar introduction to the study of botany, being the substance of a course of lectures chiefly explanatory of the Linnean system, read at the Botanic Garden, Lambeth Marsh... Now first published in the form of a dialogue betwixt a pupil and his preceptor, and illustrated by figures entirely new,* 1788–89. Only two numbers were published; its eight plates were included in *Lectures on botany as delivered in the Botanic Garden at Lambeth. By the late William Curtis FLS... Arranged from the manuscripts in the possession of his son-in-law, Samuel Curtis,* 1805, 3 volumes.

[38] The site is now part of the Brompton Hospital estate.

[39] *Journal of Botany*, vol. 40, 1902, p. 324.

[40] A. H. Haworth, *Lepidoptera Britannica*, 1803, p. 14.

Below: Plan of William Curtis's London Botanic Garden at Lambeth. (W. Curtis, *A catalogue of the British, medicinal, culinary and agricultural plants cultivated in the London Botanic Garden*, 1783).
Right: Plan of William Curtis's Botanic Garden at Brompton. (W. Curtis, *Lectures on various subjects*, vol. 3, 1805, p. 28).

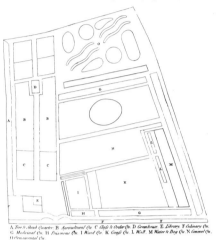

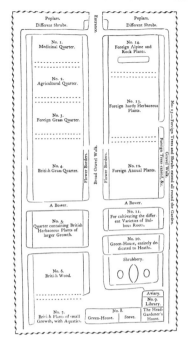

to become half partner in the Brompton Garden immediately, & while proprietor hereafter, & conductor to the best of his ability of the Bot[anical] Mag[azine] & for so doing to pay any sum that may be thought reasonable & fair, but Mr H. w[d] wish that his property in plants & Natural Hist[y] (of which a sketch is given below) ought to be blended with Mr Curtis, & that for it, *something* might be allowed as a deduction from that sum. It can hardly be thought ineligible for 2 *persons*, agreeing to become *joint partners*, in one business to write their *similar property* into *one stock*, for their natural good'.[41] The merging of their collections would form the basis of a museum of British natural history to which donations would be invited. Haworth was willing to assist in curating and demonstrating the collections.

Unfortunately nothing came of these imaginative proposals and in 1798 Curtis, now a very sick man, took William Salisbury, who had been his pupil six years earlier, into partnership. He announced the new firm of Messrs Curtis and Salisbury on the wrappers of the *Botanical Magazine*[42] and also their intention to sell plants figured in the Magazine. Salisbury had been gardener to John Symmons of Paddington who according to Curtis, had 'a collection of hardy herbaceous plants superior to most in this country'.[43] He continued the Garden after Curtis's death in 1799 but with the imminent expiry of the lease moved to Sloane Street in Chelsea about 1808, maintaining the ground at Brompton as a nursery until its disposal to the nurseryman, William Malcolm, some time before 1822. It then passed to David Ramsay, proprietor of the Swan Lane Nursery.

[41] Curtis Museum, Alton. Entomology, item 169.
[42] e.g. no. 136 of the *Botanical Magazine*.
[43] *Botanical Magazine*, 1796, plate 328.

The scientific and popular study of natural history in the eighteenth century was radically changed by the researches of Carl Linnaeus who through his systematic classifying and naming of plants brought order out of confusion. Flowering plants were grouped into 23 classes according to the number and relative length of the stamens or male organs (he provided a separate class for *Cryptogamia* or non-flowering plants). Thus *Monandria* was reserved for plants with one stamen, *Triandria* for those with three stamens and so forth. Each class was further subdivided into Orders based on the female organs or pistils. The Orders were in turn divided into genera and species. Charles Darwin's grandfather, Erasmus Darwin, celebrated this sexual system of plant classification in verses entitled *The loves of the plants* (1789), personifying the stamens as husbands, brothers, knights and squires and the pistils as wives, daughters and maids. Some naturalists like Curtis's friend, the Rev. Samuel Goodenough, were outraged: 'nothing could equal the gross prurience of Linnaeus's mind'.

This artificial classification has long since been superseded but Linnaeus's influence endures in his binomial system for the naming of organisms. Thus the Red Maple which had been turgidly recorded as *Acer americanum, folio majore, suptus argenteo, supre viridi splendente, oribus multis coccineus* was reduced by Linnaeus to the terse *Acer rubrum*. His *Species plantarum* (1753) and the tenth edition of *Systema naturae* (1758) are the basis of modern botanical and zoological nomenclature. The adoption of the new classification by William Hudson's *Flora Anglica*, John Lightfoot's *Flora Scotica* and William Curtis's *Flora Londinensis* and *Botanical Magazine* gave respectability and authority to Linnaeus's ideas in England.

The first English work to expound Linnaeus's sexual system of plants was the *Introduction to botany . . . extracted from the works of Linnaeus* (1760) by the Hammersmith nurseryman, James Lee. William Curtis, who had frequently lectured on Linnaeus, published in 1777 *Linnaeus's system of botany, so far as it relates to his classes and orders of plants*. In 1781 Erasmus Darwin asked Curtis's advice on a translation of some of Linnaeus's works which he and the other members of the exclusive Botanical Society of Lichfield wished to publish. 'They would esteem it a favour if you would honour me with a line with your opinion whether it can be translated on a better plan?'.[44] Whether the Society heeded Curtis's comments is not known but their translation appeared in 1783 as *A system of vegetables*. It did not impress Thomas Cullum of Bury in Suffolk who had seen an advance copy and told Curtis of his disappointment. 'What a curious publication is the English translation of Linn: Syst: by the Lichfield Society! The only circumstance that would make one have patience to look it over was the new plants from young Linnaeus's Supplementum'.[45]

An epidemic of caterpillars of the Brown-tail moth (*Euproctis chrysorrhoea*) in London in 1782 caused wide-spread alarm. Many feared them to be harbingers of the plague and their large closely woven webs draping trees and hedges were collected and burnt under the supervision of parish officials and churchwardens. Always an opportunist, Curtis quickly wrote *A short history of the Brown-tail moth*,

[44] Curtis Museum, Alton. Curtis letters, item 321, November 1781.
[45] *Ibid*, item 186–87, December 30, 1782.

the caterpillars of which are at present uncommonly numerous and destructive in the vicinity of the Metropolis (1782) 'to give the public a true idea of the nature of these Insects and thereby dispel their imaginary terrors'.

In the same year at the behest of his friend John Lettsom, Curtis found time to spend six weeks during the summer botanizing in the neighbourhood of Settle in Yorkshire where Lettsom had been apprenticed to a surgeon-apothecary. Curtis brought back plants for Lettsom's garden at Grove Hill and published a slim *Catalogue of certain plants, growing wild, in the environs of Settle.*

In 1782 William Forsyth, still Gardener at the Chelsea Physic Garden, and some friends formed the Society for Promoting Natural History. Meetings were held 'every month on the Monday next following the Full Moon, at seven o'clock in the evening', first at Dean's Corner House in Pimlico and later in Piccadilly and Leicester Square. Members took it in turn to preside at meetings; in 1784–85 J. E. Smith, who had doubts about the aims and organisation of the Society, was one of its four Presidents. At its thirty-second meeting on April 25, 1785, Curtis was proposed as a member. In October he was nominated to serve on the Committee for Botany. The Rev. Goodenough who had joined the Society in March that year admonished Curtis for his lack of support. 'Why have you not attended at our Society meeting yet? You & I are appointed to the Botanical Committee. Let us try what we can do for it. As I brought you into this scrape I shall *insist* on paying your Admission fee . . . . Tuesday 15th next instant is our next monthly meeting I believe . . . . Do pray be there'.[46] A penitent Curtis, no doubt anxious to make amends, obediently attended the next meeting at which he presented a paper on 'Observations on the *Sphex sabulosa* of Linnaeus', an insect he had studied in the sandpits at Charlton in Kent. At the request of the members present he had Sydenham Edwards draw the creature.[47] The attendance register of the Society shows that Curtis was never very active in its affairs. The newly formed Linnean Society rejected overtures for amalgamation and in 1822 the Society for Promoting Natural History was dissolved, and its property transferred to the more dynamic younger society.

It was dissatisfaction with the way the Society for Promoting Natural History was conducted that had led to the formation of the Linnean Society at an inaugural meeting on February 26, 1788 in the Marlborough Coffee House in Great Marlborough Street. The seven people present became its first Fellows and appointed James Edward Smith as President, Samuel Goodenough as Treasurer and Thomas Marsham as Secretary. Curtis had been urged by Goodenough to attend this meeting but was unable to do so. Goodenough in accepting his apology for absence informed him: 'Your name is put down as a *Fellow* of the Linnean Society. When we come to be a little more known, I have no doubt but you will wish to add F.L.S. to your name. We mean to keep the list of Fellows very select, only practical men & men of knowledge'.[48] Curtis was a little more active in the Linnean Society than he had been in the earlier Society;

---

[46] Curtis Museum, Alton. Curtis letters, item 232–33, November 7, 1782.
[47] The drawing is now in the library of the Linnean Society.
[48] Curtis Museum, Alton. Curtis letters, item 275, March 2, 1788.

Left: Summary in William Curtis's hand of a paper he read in 1788 to the
Society for Promoting Natural History.
Right: Page of the Roll Book of the Linnean Society with the signatures of some
of the first Fellows in 1788, including those of William Curtis,
John Sims and Robert Barclay.

he was a member of a committee to select papers in 1789, and in 1792 and 1795 a
member of the printing committee. His name frequently appears as a sponsor of
new Fellows. He presented four papers to meetings of the Society, two of which
were published in its *Transactions*.[49]

Curtis embarked on so many projects that it is not surprising that few of them
were ever completed. His *Assistant plates to the materia medica; or, figures of such plants
and animals as are used in medicine* (1786) lasted only two numbers. Its descriptions
of plants were intended to supplement textbooks on materia medica. Twenty
small engravings accompanied by lists of references in standard works were all
that appeared.

Curtis had always been interested in the agricultural use of grasses. Grasses
were, he wrote in his 1783 *Catalogue* of the London Botanic Garden, 'a much
neglected tribe . . ., out of a hundred and three species, the produce of this
country, considered by surrounding nations as most fertile in its herbage, only
one is cultivated for pasturage, and that confessedly deficient in many of the
requisites of a good grass'. One of his regular correspondents, T. G. Cullum,

[49] 'Some observations on the Natural History of the *Curcalio lapathi* and *Silpha grisea*. Two
coleopterous insects destructive to willows' (*Transactions of the Linnean Society*, vol. 1, 1791,
pp. 86–89). 'Observations on Aphides, chiefly intended to show that they are the principal
cause of blight in plants and the sole cause of the honey-dew' (*Transactions of the Linnean
Society*, vol. 6, 1802, pp. 75–94). The two unpublished papers comprise a brief note on the
larva on the Larder Beetle, *Dermestes lardarius*, and 'Some account of a mode of taking the
Anas ferina, Dun-bird or Easterling, as practised in some parts of Essex'.

PLATE 3
Iris persica. James Sowerby. Watercolour. (*Botanical Magazine*, vol. 1, 1787,
plate 1). This plant portrait provided the subject for the first plate which was
engraved in 1786.

shared his conviction. 'I wish you would engrave this summer as many as you could of the English grasses and publish them by way of supplementary or extra numbers of your *Flora*. How valuable would a compleat set of our English grasses be'.[50] Curtis sold seeds of six selected grasses from his Lambeth Garden together with a four-page leaflet: *General observations on the advantage which may result from the introduction of the seeds of our best grasses* (1787).[51] Two years later Mr Cullum had another idea. 'Would not compleat dried specimens of our English Grasses sell well, and when you made one you might make several and the profit would be clear'.[52] Grasses lend themselves to drying and pressing, an early example being G. Swayne's *Gramina pascua* (1790), a selection of 19 common pasture grasses, gathered together on six sheets. William Salisbury, Curtis's partner, sold a collection of grasses at the Brompton Botanic Garden in 1802: *Hortus siccus gramineus, or a collection of dried specimens of British grasses*.[53] The writing on the manuscript labels looks very much like Curtis's.

In addition to writing and lectures, Curtis somehow found time to botanize in the open spaces and countryside around London with friends and students. He even organized a series of field excursions, each costing two guineas, in the Battersea Meadows, Hampstead or Charlton in Kent during May to July in 1792.[54] And few people knew the London flora better than Curtis as his incidental comments in the *Flora Londinensis* abundantly testify. He had this to say, for instance, of the Lily of the Valley, *Convallaria majalis*: 'like many of those plants which are eagerly sought after, it is now become rather scarce in the neighbourhood of London. In Mr Ray's time it grew plentifully on Hampstead-Heath, but is now sparingly found there. In Lord Mansfield's wood, near the Spaniard, it may be met with in greater abundance: nor is it uncommon in the woods about Dulwich'.

Sea-kale which Curtis promoted with as much fervour as he did grasses was the subject of his last publication, *Directions for cultivating the Crambe Maritima or sea kale, for the use of the table* (1799). By selling boxes of seed from his Garden with a missionary zeal he helped to establish it as 'a truly British dish'.

William Curtis was a man of energy and ideas but undisciplined purpose. Samuel Goodenough, a friend of long standing, was convinced that 'Had Mr Curtis received a polished education, it would have proved a public benefit. One evil almost always arises from this defect. The mind, untutored, does not know how to fix itself: conscious of great and various powers, it runs from subject to subject, and never pursues any to the limit at which it was enabled to arrive. Thus Mr Curtis was perpetually forming some new design or other, without

[50] Curtis Museum, Alton. Curtis letters, item 112–13, 1780.
[51] In 1790 this leaflet was reissued in a much expanded form: *Practical observations on the British grasses, especially such as are best adapted to the laying down or improving of meadows and pastures: to which is added, an enumeration of the British grasses*. It reached a seventh edition in 1834 and a German edition was published in 1805.
[52] Curtis Museum, Alton. Curtis letters, item 186–87, December 30, 1782.
[53] The library at Kew Gardens has a copy of this rare exsiccate.
[54] 'Proposals for a course of herborizing excursions' by Mr Curtis... To commence on Monday, the 14th of May and conclude on Monday, the 9th of July 1792 (a two-page leaflet).

A plant-collecting or herborizing excursion. (Vignette from title-page of the
Flora Londinensis, vol. 1, 1777).

completing any one'.[55] Curtis, always aware of his limitations, frankly confesses
them in his unpublished autobiography.[56] 'I have no great pretensions to be
considered as a man of letters, or of great mental powers: I know myself and my
imperfections. A consciousness of my inabilities makes me diffident, and
produces in me a shyness, which some have been ready to construe into pride'.
Betty Fothergill, the niece of John Fothergill, physician and naturalist, who had
met him when a young man, judged him 'very diffident and modest'.[57] This
innate honesty and integrity may have caused him to question his religious faith.
He no longer attended regular meetings of the Society of Friends and in 1791 he
'signified by a letter that he was in the daily practice of things contrary to the
principles of friends & desired not to be considered any longer as a member of
our Society'.[58] He chose to be buried in the churchyard of St Mary's at Battersea
where he had spent so many pleasant days botanizing in nearby fields.

He was only fifty-three when he died on July 7, 1799 but in his comparatively
short life he had accomplished much. He was a visionary who, through his
publications, his lectures, his gardens at Lambeth and Brompton and perhaps
above all, through his friendships, encouraged in a vital and stimulating manner
the study and love of plants among his fellow countrymen. He was an early
conservationist who was always distressed by the destruction of plant habitats.
'The rage for building, joined to the numerous alterations perpetually making in
the environs of London, have been the means of extirpating many plants which
formerly grew plentifully around us'.[59] When a derelict site of two acres on the
South Bank near Tower Bridge was converted into a riverside marshy meadow
in 1977, no better name could be suggested for it than the William Curtis
Ecological Park.

[55] *Gentleman's Magazine*, August 1799, p. 638.
[56] This extract is quoted by Goodenough in his obituary of Curtis in the *Gentleman's
Magazine*, August 1799. He said the manuscript of the autobiography was given to John
Sims; it has since disappeared.
[57] J. J. Abraham, *Lettsom*, 1933, p. 82.
[58] Society of Friends. Devonshire House, Monthly Meeting, June 7, 1791.
[59] *Flora Londinensis: Atropa belladonna*.

~ 2 ~

THE BIRTH OF THE
BOTANICAL MAGAZINE

FOR some years William Curtis had been wondering how he was going to recoup the losses incurred by the disappointing sales of his *Flora Londinensis*. Friends and subscribers to his London Botanic Garden constantly regretted the absence of any work which they could consult for information on new exotic plants. According to Sir William Hooker,[1] it was Robert Barclay, the owner of a notable garden at Bury Hill with a conservatory and greenhouses filled with novelties, who actively encouraged Curtis to publish a periodical illustrating some of the new species. Curtis probably needed little persuasion, and the first issue of the *Botanical Magazine* was launched on February 1, 1787

---

[1] *Botanical Miscellany*, vol. 2, 1830–32, p. 122.

Paper wrapper of the first number of the
Botanical Magazine, February 1, 1787.

and for many years appeared regularly on the first day of each month. Some of the plates are dated 1786, indicating that preparation for its publication had been well under way the previous year. An expansive title page proclaimed its policy and programme to 'such ladies, gentlemen and gardeners, as wish to become scientifically acquainted with the plants they cultivate.' 'The most ornamental foreign plants, cultivated in the open ground, the green-house, and the stove, will be accurately represented in their natural colours'. Linnean Classes and Orders and binomials would be given as well as popular plant names. 'Places of growth, and times of flowering together with the most approved methods of culture' would complete this concise statement of basic information.

Each issue, priced at 1s., had three hand-coloured engravings inside its blue paper wrappers. The first number featured *Iris persica*, 'highly esteemed by all lovers of flowers', wrote Curtis, but unfortunately, still a difficult plant to grow; *Echinacea purpurea* (*Rudbeckia purpurea*)[2] from North America and Winter Aconite, *Eranthis hyemalis*. Curtis aimed his new periodical at the professional and the amateur, the knowledgeable and the ignorant. 'As our Publication seems likely to fall into the hands of such as are totally unacquainted with Botany, or botanical writings, it must plead as an apology for our often explaining many circumstances relative to plants, which may well be known to adepts in the science' (plate 8). His cultivation notes are frequently brief quotations from Philip Miller's *Gardener's dictionary*. In response to pleas from his subscribers he included the occasional florist flower but it was not until Joseph Harrison started the *Floricultural Cabinet and Florist's Magazine* in 1833 that florists had a periodical which catered for them. In 1789 he rejected a plant submitted to him for figuring in the Magazine, 'its size alone disqualifying it – nor has it in my humble opinion a sufficient share of beauty to recommend it'.[3] The size of the flower frequently bothered him. He selected *Magnolia liliiflora* with some reluctance because 'there is a magnificence about the plants of this genus which renders them unsuitable subjects of representation in a work the size of ours' (plate 390). The obvious solution was a larger plate but when he used a folded one to depict the extraordinary flower of the Bird of Paradise, *Strelitzia reginae*, recently introduced from South Africa by the Kew collector, Francis Masson, he had reservations. 'In order that we may give our readers an opportunity of seeing a coloured representation of one of the most scarce and magnificent plants introduced into this country, we have in this number deviated from our usual plan with respect to the plates, and though in so doing we shall have the pleasure of gratifying the warm wishes of many of our readers, we are not without apprehensions least others may not feel perfectly well satisfied; should it prove so, we wish such to rest assured that this is a deviation in which we shall very rarely indulge, and never but when something uncommonly beautiful or interesting presents itself' (plate 119). This first use of a folded plate displeased at least one of his subscribers – a Mrs Wilson – who regretted that the *Botanical Magazine* was not quarto size to obviate the need for them.

[2] Only accepted modern names will be given hereafter.
[3] *Gardeners' Chronicle*, October 14, 1933, p. 292.

Publish'd as the Act directs by W. Curtis, Botanic Garden, Lambeth, March, 1786

PLATE 4
Helleborus niger. Sydenham Edwards. Engraving.
(*Botanical Magazine*, vol. 1, 1787, plate 8)

This, however, was a minor quibble and sales of 3,000 copies a month[4] removed any doubts about a favourable reception. The French botanist, L'Heritier, volunteered to take a few copies to a bookseller when he returned to Paris, assuring Curtis that it would give him 'a great deal of pleasure' to do so.[5] Erasmus Darwin was mildly critical in a partisan way of the Latin diagnoses. He wished 'the characters of the plants were translated in the concise English of the translation of the Families of Plants and System of Vegetables published by our Lichfield Society . . . . I am certain it would double or quadruple the sale of Mr Curtis's Magazine. I have already recommended it to three ladies, who lament the want of Latin to understand it'.[6] James Edward Smith, reviewing the Magazine in the *Analytical Review* for 1789, praised the quality of the plates, declaring them to be superior to the 'tawdry ostentatious works of Trew' and more accurate than those in the works of Philip Miller and Mark Catesby.[7]

As many of the 36 plants that made up the first volume were either of European origin or well-established introductions, some subscribers were naturally disappointed. 'Give me leave to hint to you', protested one, 'that many persons are inclined to complain that the Numbers of this Year have contained too great a proportion of Vulgar and insignificant Plants. First or last undoubtedly every Plant, however mean, that gains admittance into the Garden, ought to be exhibited; but fewer surely on the Outset of your Work.'[8] European plants also dominated the second volume and in 1789 Curtis felt it necessary to defend his selection. 'It has been suggested by some of our readers, that too many common plants, like the present [*Centaurea montana*], are figured in this work. We wish it to be understood, that the professed design of the Botanical Magazine is to exhibit representations of such' (plate 77). Preference would always be given to plants in general cultivation rather than to rarities. Nevertheless, he insisted that 'one-third of the plants figured, have some pretensions to novelty'.

Curtis had a genuine affection for those familiar flowers that had been well-loved ornaments of English gardens for many centuries – the daisy (plate 228), the antirrhinum (plate 207), the Mock Orange (plate 391) and the Madonna Lily (plate 278). But he was catholic in his taste and eclectic in his choice. 'Some plants have a claim on our attention for their utility, some for their beauty, and some for the singularity of their structure, and the wonderful nature of their oeconomy' (plate 254). He was delighted to introduce *Dendranthema grandiflorum* (plate 327), confidently predicting that it 'promises to become an acquisition highly valuable'. He recognised the popularity of the Cape flora: *Erica, Gladiolus, Mesembryanthemum* and *Pelargonium*; over a hundred South African plants were drawn for the Magazine before his death in 1799. Hardy trees and shrubs from eastern North America were represented by some 50 plates. The return of

---

[4] *Gentleman's Magazine*, July 1799, p. 629.

[5] Curtis Museum, Alton. Curtis letters, item 261–62, July 4, 1787.

[6] Erasmas Darwin to J. C. Lettsom, October 8, 1787. In T. J. Pettigrew, *Memoirs of the life and writings of the late John Coakley Lettsom*, vol. 3, 1871, p. 118.

[7] J. E. Smith, *Tracts relating to natural history*, 1798, pp. 179–80.

[8] Curtis Museum, Alton. Curtis letters, item 267–68, December 19, 1787, (J. Butler, Andover).

Captain Cook in H.M.S. *Endeavour* in 1772 introduced the floristic wealth of the Southern Hemisphere, and the establishment of a convict settlement in New South Wales in 1788 offered opportunities for a more leisurely and systematic collecting of Australian plants. The first Australian plant selected by Curtis was *Hardenbergia violacea* (plate 263). In 1792 Curtis persuaded Samuel Tolfrey to let him have some of the specimens of soil brought back from Botany Bay, suspecting that they may contain seeds. 'Accordingly in the Spring of 1793, I exposed them in shallow pans, on a gentle tan heat, keeping them duly watered; in the course of the Summer they yielded me fourteen plants, most of which were altogether new, and among others the species of *Goodenia*, [*Scaevola albida*], here figured' (plate 287). Curtis published descriptions of some 20 plants from China and Japan, nine from the Indian subcontinent and nine from the West Indies. The number of exotic plants ranges between one-third and one-half in most volumes; in the last two volumes published before the close of the eighteenth century the proportion increased to two-thirds.

The botanical artist and engraver, Henry C. Andrews, started the first serious rival to the *Botanical Magazine* with his *Botanist's Repository for New and Rare Plants* in 1797. His justification was that 'the greatest part [of the *Botanical Magazine*], as its title page indicates, consists of those well-known, common plants, long cultivated in our gardens'.[9] His father-in-law, John Kennedy, a partner in the famous Hammersmith nursery of Lee and Kennedy, wrote most of the descriptions in the first five volumes. The inevitable clash between the two rivals led J. B. Gawler, a regular contributor to the *Botanical Magazine*, to write anonymously *Recensio plantarum; review of the plants hitherto figured in the Botanical Repository* (1801) which purported 'to correct the misnomers' in the first two volumes of Andrews's publication.

Curtis obtained specimens for his Magazine from the stock of his gardens at Lambeth and Brompton, and from London nurserymen such as Barr of Ball's Pond Road, Colvill of King's Road, Chelsea, James Gordon and Thompson of Mile End, Grimwood (later Grimwood and Wykes) of Kensington, Lee and Kennedy of Hammersmith, Loddiges of Hackney, Whitley (later Whitley and Barritt) of Old Brompton and Richard Williams of Turnham Green. Amongst the donations from private gardens were a calceolaria from the Duke of Northumberland at Syon House, a carnation – 'Franklin's Tartar' – raised by Mr Franklin of Lambeth, 'an ingenious cultivator of these flowers', *Viola pedata* from Thomas Sykes of Hackney who specialized in North American plants and *Trifolium incarnatum* from John Symmons of Paddington.

There is no evidence for the suggestion some writers have made that Curtis drew some of the plates; indeed his son-in-law, Samuel Curtis, reported that 'he never could draw well himself'.[10] During his lifetime, Edwards and Sowerby were solely responsible for the artwork.[11]

Sydenham Teast Edwards (1768–1819), born at Usk in Gwent, came to the

---

[9] *Botanist's Repository for new and rare plants*, preface to vol. 1, 1797.

[10] S. Curtis, 'Memoir of the life and writings of the late Mr. William Curtis', 1828, p. ix.

[11] This is confirmed in a note to subscribers published in 1809 and repeated in 1811, (inserted after plates 1232 and 1366 respectively in the Kew set of the *Botanical Magazine*).

Passiflora coerulea (plate 28). James Sowerby's original drawing was modified by the engraver (see opposite).

attention of Curtis through his youthful attempts to copy plates in the *Flora Londinensis*. Impressed by the boy's obvious talents, Curtis invited him to London for further training and in a short while he was drawing and engraving for the *Flora Londinensis* itself. He was Curtis's companion on many field excursions, learning to draw animals, birds and insects as well as flowers.

James Sowerby (1757–1822) was already employed as a colourist, artist and engraver by Curtis when Edwards arrived on the scene. He had been trained at the Royal Academy and afterwards apprenticed to the marine painter Richard Wright. Through making sketches of flowers for inclusion in his paintings, he met Curtis and followed Kilburn as the principal artist of the *Flora Londinensis*.

A flower painter such as Sowerby or Edwards whose aim is scientific accuracy rather than a pretty composition is more correctly known as a botanical artist.

[35]

He has to subordinate his artistic expression to the requirements of the botanist, adapting his drawing, if required, to emphasize or clarify any significant or distinguishing characteristics in a plant. Watercolours and pen and ink, rather than oils, are the media normally used to provide the purity and delicacy of touch he seeks to achieve. Infinite patience is desirable, not only in recording the minutiae of plants but also in waiting for the appropriate seasons to paint them. Lilian Snelling painted the inflorescence of *Prunus webbii* (N.S. plate 118) in 1936 and its fruit two years later. And this gentle occupation is not without its occasional hazards. When Matilda Smith drew the orchid, *Bulbophyllum beccarii*, (plate 6567) in a greenhouse at Kew, she was overpowered by its offensive smell and became quite ill as a result. Most of the *Botanical Magazine* portraits were made from the actual plants but now and then, in the absence of specimens, reliable drawings were copied. Sir William Hooker borrowed drawings from Sir Joseph Banks and W. T. Aiton; Sir Joseph Hooker even made use of the stylized drawings of Indian artists; *Aloe bainesii* (plate 6848) was based on a photograph.

A distinction must be made between botanical drawing where accuracy is paramount and horticultural drawing where some licence is permissible. The gardener expects a reasonable representation of a flower but does not demand the detail essential for the botanist. This freedom was sometimes abused by unscrupulous nurserymen who sought to promote the sale of their plants by getting artists to enhance their more attractive features.

Curtis never lacked unsolicited advice and foremost among his critics was, inevitably, Sir Thomas Frankland. In one letter he harangued poor Curtis at considerable length, reciting what he conceived to be the essentials of good flower drawing:

'The Drawings should be executed in the stile of Engraving with precise distinct strokes, which tho' not so beautiful as if softened will be far more intelligible to the Engraver.

Great care should be taken not to represent the plants as if flattened by Drying.

No stunted specimen ought to be figured for the sake of getting it within the bounds of the plate . . . .

A good *outline* is the thing most to be aimed at . . . .

No *opaque colours* should be used as they require too much skill & time to give them a proper appearance. The intention of engraving the shadows is that they may appear thro the *transparent* colours . . .' .[12]

An anonymous correspondent thought 'it would be an improvement if there were less engraving in some flowers especially in white ones, and if ye shading were left to ye colourist'.[13]

The drawings of Sowerby and Edwards were reproduced by copper plate engraving. The engraver either cut out the design in shallow grooves on the polished surface of a copper plate with a graving tool or burin, or covered the plate with an acid-resistant wax ground through which the design was drawn with a needle and the exposed copper subsequently bitten by acid. Being a cheap

[12] Curtis Museum, Alton. Curtis letters, item 202–03, not dated.
[13] *Ibid*, item 280–81, March 31, 1788.

and less laborious method of engraving, etching was frequently used in illustrated works such as the *Botanical Magazine*.

James Sowerby's *English Botany* demonstrates what a dextrous engraver could accomplish; the lines are economical, unmarred by any excess of cross hatching, and admirably suited for subsequent hand-colouring. After a copper plate had been engraved, it was inked, the surface wiped so that the ink was retained only in the incised lines, and then a paper impression taken in a press.[14]

Francis Sansom took Milton's place as engraver on the *Flora Londinensis*, drawing as well as engraving some of the early plates. He engraved all the plates in the *Botanical Magazine* for William Curtis. The 119 plates in Curtis's posthumously published *Lectures on botany* (1805) are also by Sansom who eventually went blind through the constant strain of this close and exacting work.

Thirty people were engaged in colouring the plates in the *Botanical Magazine* under the supervision of William Graves.[15] It was customary to employ young women and children in this repetitive work. Four of Samuel Curtis's daughters became skilled colourists of flower plates. James Sowerby recruited his whole family to help him colour his *English Botany*; the children graduated from the elementary colouring of the fragment of ground or 'dirt' on some of the compositions to more demanding work, but always under their father's supervision.

Ackermann's Repository of Arts in the Strand was a kind of factory for the mass production of coloured prints. An efficient organisation of labour was essential to cope with the vast quantities of prints that Ackermann and other publishers produced. The team of colourists sat at tables, usually applying a single colour to each print, having before them a specimen coloured print as a guide. A master colourist would, if required, add the finishing touches. In a letter of December 27, 1836, Francis Bauer, the Kew botanical artist, asked W. J. Hooker for 'a couple of proof prints, on the proper paper for colouring. I will prepare them as samples for the colourers, which [are] easier for them to work from, than from the original drawings'. The routine had changed very little when Lovell Reeve and Company explained the procedure adopted by their small group of colourists in the 1920s. 'A regular colourer prefers to work in hundreds of the same plate, one colour at a time and one plate after another, in a purely mechanical way. An expert colourer working full time may perhaps colour 200 8vo plates a week, more or less, according to the number of colours and the amount of surface and detail; but their rate vary very much with their personality'.[16] The application of water colour to prints is not as simple as it may seem. Filling in areas of a print with solid blocks of colour which were 'thick enough to hide both the lights and the shades' was deprecated by the author of the *Method of learning to draw in perspective* (1735) who declared the result was 'like

[14] Black ink was normal but on some of the plates in the *Botanical Magazine* green or red ink has been used as a foundation colour (plates 68–69, 92, 134, 139, 922, 975, 1341–42).
[15] *Gentleman's Magazine*, July 1799, p. 629.
[16] Royal Botanic Gardens, Kew. Library (Archives). 'Publishers' notes on the production of Curtis's *Botanical Magazine*, January 11, 1922.'

a Penny Picture, where there is nothing to be seen but a Jargon of Reds, Blues and Yellows'. Transparent washes of watercolour were preferred to opaque colours which tended to obscure finely engraved lines. A coat of gum water could be added to those parts of the finished print where a gloss was required to emphasize shadow. With a relentless pressure of work it was no mean achievement that a creditable level of care and finish was maintained by most colourists. Where there were lapses it should be remembered that the low wages paid did not encourage them to excel.

The first plate in the *Botanical Magazine, Iris persica*, is delicately and deftly coloured with transparent washes. Extra care was taken with special presentation copies. 'I wish to make up three sets of the Magazine for presents executed in a superior style – yours is one of them – they took up more time than I expected'.[17] The *Botanical Magazine* preserved a splendid tradition of hand colouring from its first issue in February 1787 until 1948 when rising costs and a scarcity of colourists compelled a change to mechanical colour printing.

Most of the drawings prepared by Sowerby and Edwards are accurate and

---

[17] British Museum (Natural History). Botany Library. W. Curtis to an unknown correspondent, November 27, 1798.

Symplocarpus foetidus or Skunk Cabbage. Left: By Sydenham Edwards (plate 836). Right: Redrawn by W. J. Hooker, who considered the earlier drawing unsatisfactory (plate 3224).

PLATE 6
Rosa centifolia 'Muscosa'. Sydenham Edwards. Engraving. (*Botanical Magazine*,
vol. 2, 1788, plate 69). Red rather than black ink has been used in the printing
of this plate.

though no botanical dissections were added to the plates, they usually delineated the essential characters of a plant adequately for identification purposes. There were failures, of course. One anonymous letter to Curtis while conceding that 'the plates, for ye price are good', complained that 'ye drawings are not all that accurate'.[18] J. E. Smith was unhappy about the Moss Rose. 'The expanded flower is ill drawn, and too uniform in colour, and the stalk of much too high a pink hue'.[19] Subsequent editors of the Magazine occasionally corrected errors in earlier plates. Sir Joseph Hooker disliked Curtis's portrayal of *Helleborus lividus* (plate 72). 'That figure is so unsatisfactory, and indeed inaccurate, representing the sepals as acute, that I have deemed it right to introduce a better' (plate 7903).

These flaws did not detract from the Magazine's popularity; the demand for it was sufficient to warrant reprinting the earlier volumes.[20] Samuel Curtis calculated that with all these reprints upwards of 5,000 copies of each of the early numbers were sold.[21] William Curtis, he said, had boasted that whereas the *Flora Londinensis* had won him 'praise', the Magazine had 'brought him pudding'. After several abortive projects Curtis had, at last, found one that had stability and the promise of permanence. Yet he was not wholly content. His *Flora* was foundering, the apparent hostility of J. E. Smith still rankled, and his health was deteriorating. 'I would I were near you that I might halloo in your ear & rally your spirits a little', wrote Goodenough encouragingly. 'You cannot mend the matter be it ever as bad or even worse than you make it, by bowing down your mind to drooping forebodings & melancholy. Up man, & hope for the best. You really are extremely hypochondriac, while you are convincing yourself you are not . . . . You have no malevolent enemies. Everybody likes you & is your friend'.[22] Nine months after that letter was written Curtis was dead. In his will he requested that the *Botanical Magazine* be continued 'in the same manner it has hitherto been' under the editorship of his friend, Dr John Sims.

[18] Curtis Museum, Alton. Curtis letters, item 280–81, March 31, 1788.
[19] J. E. Smith, *Tracts relating to natural history*, 1798, p. 186.
[20] Vol. 1 was re-issued in 1793; vol. 2 in 1796, vol. 3 in 1797, vol. 4 in 1795, vol. 5 in 1796 and vol. 6 in 1793.
[21] S. Curtis, 'Memoir of the life and writings of the late Mr. William Curtis', 1828, p. xxiii.
[22] Curtis Museum, Alton. Curtis letters, item 316, October 5, 1798.

3

JOHN SIMS IN CHARGE

WILLIAM Curtis's will stipulated that his brother, Thomas, should continue to work for the *Botanical Magazine* on the same salary and allowances. According to a note written by Professor J. S. Henslow in the Kew Library copy of the Magazine, Thomas Curtis conducted the Magazine from plate 450 (1800) until Dr Sims assumed editorship in 1801.[1] Thomas operated from 3 St George's Crescent 'near the obelisk at the bottom of Blackfriars Road' to which William Curtis had moved some time between June 1787 and June 1788. Thomas's eldest daughter, Mary, eventually married George Graves, the future owner of the *Flora Londinensis*.

Curtis had left sufficient material to conduct the Magazine for five years[2] – nearly 200 drawings according to R. J. Thornton.[3] John Sims in the preface of his first volume as editor, now entitled *Curtis's Botanical Magazine*, revealed that he intended making little use of them 'principally from a desire to preserve them as entire as possible for the service of the proprietors, in case of emergency, and with a wish to indulge our botanical readers with a representation and description of some of the novel and curious plants which are annually introduced, particularly from the Cape of Good Hope'.

John Sims (1749–1831), who probably first met Curtis when they both attended the Quaker school at Burford, had a medical practice at Dunmow in Essex, was a Fellow of the Royal Society and an early Fellow of the Linnean Society.[4] Not withstanding his promise to edit the Magazine along the same lines as the late owner, he proceeded to make certain alterations from vol. 15 (1801), the first to appear under his name. Wishing to resolve the confusion in the nomenclature of Iridaceae, he engaged the services of John Bellenden Gawler (who later changed his name to John Bellenden Ker) to work on this group of plants. Gawler, who signed his contributions with the letter 'G', described many of the new Cape introductions: *Gladiolus, Ixia, Moraea* and *Watsonia*. He discussed all the irises figured in vol. 18, but by vol. 20 (1804) his contributions had become fewer and shorter. Sydenham Edwards was still the principal artist.

The small margin of profit and the 100 per cent increase in the price of paper necessitated raising the price of the Magazine from 1s. to 1s.6d., but as a compensatory gesture an extra plate was added to each number.[5] At the same

[1] From plate 557 (April 1, 1802) some of the plates carried the imprint, 'Pub by T. Curtis'.
[2] *Gentleman's Magazine*, July 1799, p. 629; *Botanical Magazine*, vol. 15, 1801, preface.
[3] W. Curtis, *Lectures on botany*, vol. 3, 1805, p. 22.
[4] The signatures of Sims and Curtis appear on the same page of the Linnean Society Roll Book (see p. 25).
[5] Sims stated that W. Curtis had contemplated raising the price to 1s.6d.

John Sims (1749–1831)
by C. R. Leslie, 1824. Mezzotint.

time the price of numbers already published was increased to 1s.3d. From about no. 188 the number of plates in each issue rose to eight and the price to 3s.; by no. 255, about seven years after Sims had assumed editorship, 3s.6d. was being charged for each issue but the editor assured readers that the Magazine 'may still be considered as the cheapest Publication of the kind extant'. Some 20 years later Samuel Curtis was still unsure of the wisdom of these rapid price increases. 'Although it had a very extensive sale after this increased quantity [of plates], and advanced price, still many of those who spent their shilling per month would not go so far as three shillings and sixpence, so that the sale of the current number was very much reduced'.[6] The services of Stephen Couchman of Throgmorton Street who had printed the Magazine from its inception (then Fry and Couchman) were retained, and from vol. 27 (1808) the publisher was H. D. Symonds of 20 Paternoster Row and two years later Sherwood, Neely and Jones at the same address.

William Curtis had reluctantly used a folded plate and Sims found himself obliged to do likewise to do justice to *Amaryllis belladona* (plate 733). When he saw the splendid South African plant, *Protea cynaroides* – years later the plant collector, E. H. Wilson, enthusiastically declared it to be 'the handsomest inflorescence in the world' – Sims succumbed again. 'We have seldom so far deviated from our usual plan as to give double plates, but for the sake of such a representation of so magnificent a flower as the present we run no risk of incurring blame' (plate 770). The double or folded plate counted as two single plates but Sims assured subscribers that 'the expense and trouble of this number are fully equal to those which contain eight [plates], and, were the labours of our artists adequately rewarded, would be considerably greater'. Thereafter Sims introduced folded plates with an easy conscience; there were, for example, four in each of vols. 19, 23 and 24. Some folded plates combined a drawing of the inflorescence with a line-drawing of the entire plant.[7]

Floral and other diagnostic details which were frequently added to plates in other contemporary magazines were seldom encountered in the *Botanical*

[6] S. Curtis, 'Memoir of the life and writings of the late Mr. William Curtis', 1828, p. xxiii.
[7] For example: plates 903 (*Nelumbo*), 1081 (*Dracaena*) and 1260 (*Yucca*).

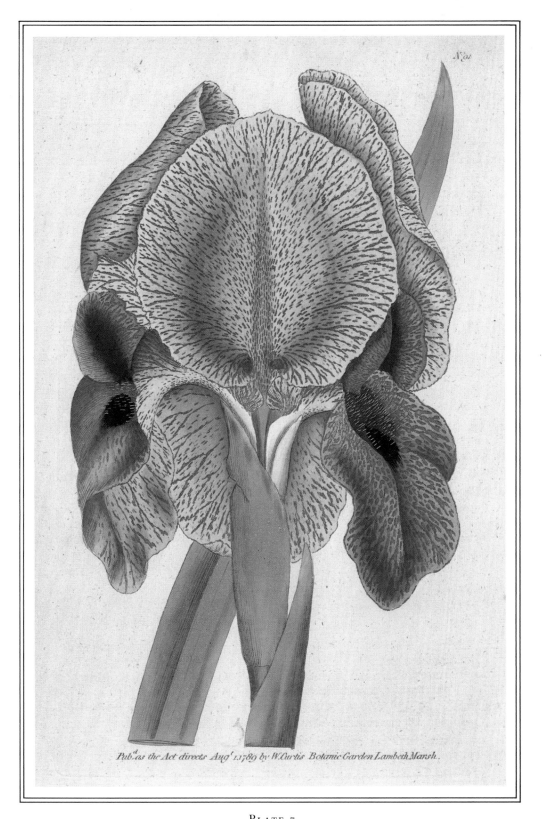

Pub.^d as the Act directs Augt 1.1789 by W.Curtis Botanic Garden Lambeth Marsh.

PLATE 7
Iris susiana. James Sowerby. Engraving. (*Botanical Magazine*, vol. 3, 1790,
plate 91). This iris has been grown in European gardens ever since 1573 when it
was sent by the Austrian ambassador in Turkey to Vienna.

Magazine. Dissections were given for the first time in vol. 34 (1811)[8] and although they were included from time to time it was not until W. J. Hooker became editor that they were a routine feature.

Plate 1345 in vol. 33 (1811), illustrating *Haworthia attenuata* from the Cape, was the first plate to carry the imprint, 'published by S. Curtis, Walworth'. Samuel Curtis (1779–1860), son of a surgeon, was first cousin to William Curtis and married his daughter, Sarah Caustin, on October 19, 1801. Samuel Curtis had recently taken over the nursery formerly belonging to his brother-in-law, James Maddock. (It was in Maddock's nursery in 1794 that William Curtis had seen single and double varieties of *Narcissus* × *tenuior* for the first time (plate 379).) About 1805 he purchased Glazenwood near Braintree in Essex where he cultivated hardy fruit trees as well as ornamental plants on its 40 ha (100 acres). For an annual subscription of two guineas the public were admitted on Tuesdays and Fridays to wander through its 'flower-beds, shrubberies, groves and walks' and to admire 'the splendid *Wisteria consequana* [*W. sinensis*], extending 70 yards in length by 30 feet high; the lovely trumpet-shaped red and orange blossoms of the *Bignonia capreolata* [*Doxantha capredata*], several varieties of magnolia, amongst which *Magnolia grandiflora* towers to a height of 30 feet'.[9]

Also in 1805 Samuel Curtis published a collection of his late father-in-law's lectures, *Lectures on botany, as delivered in the Botanic Garden at Lambeth* in three volumes with a 'Sketch of the life and writings of the late Mr William Curtis' by R. J. Thornton in the third volume.

Samuel Curtis had something of his father-in-law's enterprise and initiative. In 1806 he started publishing *Beauties of Flora* which was completed in 1820 with ten large plates in aquatint and stipple after drawings by Thomas Baxter and Clara Maria Pope. All but two dahlia plates have landscape backgrounds much like those in Thornton's celebrated *Temple of Flora* (1798–1807). There was no explanatory text for this exceedingly rare and beautiful work and the engravings were available singly at 12s. each or £5 the set. He was associated with the *Botanical Magazine* through his wife's inheritance of the publication; after her death in 1827 he became proprietor.

His first crisis as its publisher was the desertion of J. B. Gawler, his artist Sydenham Edwards, and engraver Francis Sansom, to start a rival periodical, the *Botanical Register*. Edwards's departure was the most serious loss. After Curtis's death he had continued to draw for the Magazine and also found time to undertake other commissions. He illustrated Alexander MacDonald's *Complete dictionary of practical gardening* (1807), republished in 1812 as *The new botanic garden* and *The new flora Britannica*. It seems likely that Edwards made use of some of his original sketches for the Magazine. There is, for example, more than an accidental similarity between the illustration of *Strelitzia reginae* in the *Botanical Magazine* and the same plant in MacDonald's book.

The first intimation of some unease in the relationship between Edwards and the Magazine can be detected in a handbill addressed to subscribers in 1809. This announces the fact that the 'Botanical Magazine certainly owes its

[8] Plates 1405 (*Lilium monadelphum*), and 1411 (*Liatris spicata*).
[9] *Illustrated London News*, July 1, 1843.

reputation, in great measure to the excellence of the figures, *nearly the whole* of which have been executed by Mr Sydenham Edwards. As it has appeared to him that attempts have been repeatedly made to deprive him of his due share of the credit arising from these figures – at one time by representing that a *large proportion* of them were drawn by Mr Sowerby – and at another by insinuating that such only as have his name affixed to them were drawn by Sydenham Edwards, it is with pleasure that we comply with his request of laying before our readers an accurate statement of the whole of the figures that were not executed by himself'. Then follows the surprising admission that 12 plates with Sowerby's name on them[10] were in fact drawn by Edwards. With the exception of 55 specified plates, all the unsigned drawings were by Edwards; out of some 1,200 plates only 67 were Sowerby's work. Two years later this statement was re-issued with a concluding paragraph to placate an obviously irate Sowerby. 'That hand-bill was published in haste, without reflecting that some expressions contained in it might be hurtful to the feelings of a friend for whom we have ever entertained the highest respect and esteem. And Mr Edwards is himself convinced that the misrepresentations there complained of . . . did not originate in any enmity towards him'.

Samuel Curtis never revealed the cause of the rift but 13 years after it had taken place he was still bitter about it. 'It would have been more in unison with common gratitude, and more to his own peace of mind, in his last illness, if he had not been persuaded to begin a work in direct opposition to the Botanical Magazine, by which he had risen, and which work, after his patron was dead, was the support of his widow, daughter and grandchildren. Besides, there was no necessity for such a work, as the public were well satisfied with the Magazine, in every respect, without burthening science with another exactly the same except the title, which Mr Gawler and Mr Edwards to distinguish it from "Magazine" called "Register" and charged it at a higher price'.[11] Commencing in 1815 the *Register* was published monthly by James Ridgway with eight plates in each number which cost 4s. The text by Gawler was much fuller than that in the Magazine and dissections were given for every plant figured. Edwards who was described on the buff-coloured paper wrappers as the 'late designer to the Botanical Magazine' drew all the 349 plates for the first four volumes (1815–1819), but Sansom's eyesight was now so weak that he could engrave only eight of them. When Edwards died in 1819 he was succeeded by M. Hart.

For some years the *Botanical Magazine* was the only illustrated periodical of its kind but that exclusive position was soon to be challenged. The first competitor was Henry C. Andrew's *Botanist's Repository* in 1797. J. E. Smith started *Exotic Botany* in 1804 because Curtis and Andrews could not 'keep pace with the botanical riches daily flowing in upon us'.[12] The *Botanical Register* in 1815 was followed two years later by the *Botanical Cabinet*, launched by Conrad Loddiges, owner of one of the largest and most prosperous nurseries in the country and a generous contributor of material to the *Botanical Magazine*. With the com-

[10] Plates 18, 23, 25, 27, 29, 30, 31, 34, 35, 36, 38 and 43.

[11] S. Curtis, 'Memoir of the life and writings of the late Mr. William Curtis', 1828, pp. xi–xii.

[12] *Exotic Botany*, 1804, preface.

plimentary copy of the first issue he sent to John Sims, he enclosed a conciliatory note beseeching him not to view it as being in opposition to the Magazine. 'Such an idea never entered our minds, nor can anything be farther from our wishes. The boundless variety of the vegetable world is doubtless sufficient to afford subjects for us all'.[13] For 16 years it came out monthly in two simultaneous issues: a large paper copy, fully coloured at 5s., and an octavo version with partly-coloured plates at 2s.6d. James Ridgway, not content with publishing the *Botanical Register*, took on Robert Sweet's *British Flower Garden* in 1823. Two years later the *Botanic Garden*, under the aegis of Benjamin Maund, publisher, printer, bookseller and chemist at Bromsgrove in Worcestershire, made its début in a large paper issue at 1s.6d. and a small paper version at 1s. – the first indication of a fall in periodical prices.

Threatened by such competitors who were partly responsible for a continuing decline in subscriptions, both the proprietor and the editor of the *Botanical Magazine* were acutely sensitive to any criticism. Their resentment towards the *Botanical Register* was sooner or later bound to explode. 'We have been sometimes blamed for giving plants which have been before figured in the Botanical Register,[14] a censure to which no one of our numbers has been so much exposed, as the present. In this case, however, our drawing being made and engraved before the publication of it in the Register' (plate 2005).

As the plates are not signed, it is not known who were the artists used by the Magazine after the defection of Sydenham Edwards. In all probability they had been done by Edwards while he was their artist. This is suggested by the following apologia in the Magazine in 1818. 'The following season of plants is fugitive, the recurrences of opportunity often uncertain, which, united with other circumstances, makes it necessary to accumulate our drawings long before they can be used; and the artists of the first eminence, who have been always employed in drawing for the *Botanical Magazine*, are paid too highly for their labours to allow of these being thrown aside' (plate 2005). The drawing for plate 1824 (1816), for instance, 'was taken several years ago at the late Mr Grimwood's nursery'; no artist's name is given but it must surely have been Edwards. After Edwards's death in 1819 his earlier drawings were frequently published and duly acknowledged.[15]

Sansom was replaced as the Magazine's engraver by Messrs Weddell of Walworth. Several members of this prolific family of botanical engravers engraved the plates from 1815 to 1826.[16] There was a perceptible improvement in the hand-colouring as Weddell probably employed a different team of colourists.

[13] Royal Botanic Gardens, Kew. Library (Archives). Letters to John Sims, item 29, April 16, 1817.
[14] A correspondent to the *Gardener's Magazine* in 1828 (p. 163) makes a spirited attack on what he considered to be the *Botanical Magazine's* repetition of plants already figured elsewhere.
[15] For example: plates 2151, 2159, 2187, 2195, 2209, 2220, 2233, etc.
[16] H. H. Weddell aquatinted five plates for Samuel Curtis's *Monograph on the genus Camellia*, 1819.

PLATE 8

Paeonia tenuifolia. Sydenham Edwards. Engraving by F. Sansom. (*Curtis's Botanical Magazine*, vol. 23, 1806, plate 926). This fern-leaved peony, also known as the Adonis peony, was introduced to England from the Caucasus in 1765.

From vol. 43 (1815–16) which began a New Series,[17] the number of plates in a volume doubled – in order, perhaps, to counter the attractions of the *Botanical Register*. In 1818 John Curtis took up residence as botanical artist. His manifest competence leads one to believe that he was the same John Curtis (1791–1862) – not related to either William or Samuel Curtis – who executed such remarkable drawings in *British entomology* (1824–39), depicting insects in association with their host plants.

These were very difficult times for the *Botanical Magazine* – in 1828 the number of subscribers had dropped below a thousand[18] – but it still had its loyal supporters, among them The Hon. and Rev. William Herbert. His father, Henry Herbert, Earl of Carnarvon, had introduced several species of *Hippeastrum* into cultivation at the family seat at Highclere. The first *Hippeastrum* cultivated in England was probably *H. reginae* which, according to the Magazine which figured it in 1799 (plate 453), flowered in Thomas Fairchild's nursery at Hoxton in 1728. Lord Carnarvon's passion for this flower influenced William Herbert's life-long study of Amaryllidaceae. In his garden at Spofforth near Manchester, where he was Rector, he cultivated, classified and drew genera belonging to Amaryllidaceae and also Iridaceae. He investigated aspects of genetics and plant breeding and was a pioneer hybridist. His first major contribution to the Magazine was *Crinum zeylanicum* (plate 2121 (1820)) for which he drew the plate and wrote eight pages of text. Sims came to rely upon him for descriptions of bulbous plants.

Many plates and taxonomic commentary in the *Botanical Magazine* until 1841 testify to his industry. With commendable impartiality he also contributed to the *Botanical Register* whose publisher, James Ridgway, issued in 1821 his *Appendix to the Botanical Register and Botanical Magazine. Intended to bind up with either of those works. Containing a botanical arrangement and description of the plants heretofore included under the genera Amaryllis, Cyrtanthus, Crinum and Pancratium; with general observations and directions for their cultivation.* The wrapper recommends that 'the Appendix may be placed at the End of any Volume, but most properly the 48th of the *Botanical Magazine*, and the 7th of the *Botanical Register*'. His major work was *Amaryllidaceae* (1837) in which he enumerated many of the hybrid hippeastrums raised by him at Spofforth. H. H. Weddell engraved all the author's drawings in this book which is still highly regarded by botanists. Vol. 65 (1838–39) of the *Botanical Magazine* is dedicated to him.

For the convenience of its readers, the Magazine issued cumulative indexes, the first being to the first ten volumes in 1795.[19] In 1816 a *General index* to the first 42 volumes was published with the suggestion that the preceding plates be bound in systematic order and the text numerically by plate numbers.[20] This index was in turn superseded by another *General index* in 1828, extending the

[17] For the convenience of existing subscribers, the original plate numbers were continued.
[18] S. Curtis, 'Memoir of the life and writings of the late Mr. William Curtis', 1828 p. xxiv.
[19] The cumulative index to the first 20 volumes in 1805 was arranged in two sequences under Latin and English plant names.
[20] H. J. Brookes rearranged all the plates published up to 1840 in his copies of the *Botanical Magazine, Botanical Register, British Flower Garden* and the phanerogams in *English*

coverage to vol. 52. It provided English and Latin indexes and a systematic index following Sprengel in the latest edition of Linnaeus's *Systema vegetabilium*. Samuel Curtis contributed his informative 'Memoir of the life and writings of the late Mr William Curtis'.

In 1826, the final editorial year of John Sims, now in his late seventies, J. C. Loudon reviewed the merits of the *Botanical Magazine* and the *Botanical Register*.[21] He praised Sydenham Edwards 'for the skill he possessed of transferring an accurate resemblance of the largest plants to the small space of an octavo page'. He commended the drawings of John Curtis, was unenthusiastic about the Magazine's hand-colouring and dismissed the text as meagre. The plates of the *Botanical Register*, on the other hand, were 'better filled by their subjects', and the text reflected modern botanical thought whereas the Magazine was 'a register for the old school of botany'. The injection of new ideas and the displacement of lethargy by liveliness began to transform the *Botanical Magazine* only with the appointment of W. J. Hooker as editor in 1827.

During all the years Sims was editor there was no diminution in the flow of new plants reaching Europe, firmly bedded in tubs lined up on the decks of sailing ships or sent as packets of seeds through the post. The number of tender exotics increased as methods for ensuring their survival during long sea voyages improved.

Favoured by a short ocean crossing and by a similar climate, plants from the temperate regions of North America were always in great demand with British gardeners. Of some 500 different species of hardy trees and shrubs brought to England by the end of the seventeenth century, 350 of them came from North America. Certainly these proportions had not changed by the nineteenth century when J. C. Loudon, with characteristic thoroughness, calculated that well over half of the trees and shrubs imported between 1800 and 1830 had originated in the United States and Canada. Drawings of 60 of the American plants, diligently collected by John Fraser and his son between the years 1785 and 1817, were presented to readers of the *Botanical Magazine*.[22] Fraser's *Rhododendron catawbiense* (plate 1671) which he introduced in 1809 was selected by breeders as the main parent for a spectacular progeny of hardy hybrids. W. J. Hooker was impressed by 'his skilful method of packing [which] enabled him to transmit, uninjured, many living plants, to which the hazards of a long sea voyage had always, previously, proved fatal'. The nursery which his son John established near Ramsgate in Kent was purchased in 1835 by Samuel Curtis's son, William. John Lyon, who was in North America at the end of the eighteenth century, held his first major sale of plants in London in 1806. The catalogue of 34 pages listed what was probably the biggest collection of North American trees and shrubs ever brought to England by one man. David Douglas was a protégé of W. J. Hooker who wrote shortly after the news of his tragic death that 'there is scarcely a spot of ground deserving the name of garden which does not owe

Botany alphabetically in one sequence under genera. The 78 volumes are now in the library of the Linnean Society.

[21] *Gardener's Magazine*, vol. 1, 1826, pp. 59–60.
[22] *Companion to the Botanical Magazine*, vol. 2, 1836, pp. 303–05.

many of its most powerful attractions to the living roots and seeds which have been sent by him to the Horticultural Society of London' from North America. Clarkias, godetias, lupins, the American currant and the Californian poppy are just a few of his discoveries to become garden favourites. In 1926 it was calculated that out of the 9,000 plates published in the *Botanical Magazine*, 1,000 were devoted to North American plants and many of those can be assigned to Douglas, a man of discrimination as well as dedication.

The New World was generously treated while Sims was editor: 270 plants from North America, nearly 200 from Central and South America and just over 100 from the West Indies. Mexico yielded many horticultural delights: dahlias, salvias and zinnias, for example. The dahlia reached Madrid in 1789 and Kew's first attempts to grow it were unsuccessful as were the efforts of the nurseryman, John Fraser, with *Dahlia coccinea*, the first dahlia to be illustrated in the *Botanical Magazine* (plate 762). But, by 1806, 55 varieties had been bred and 11 years later when two drawings were made of *Dahlia × hortorum* (plate 1885 a & b) its popularity was firmly established. Samuel Curtis's *Beauties of Flora* boasted two splendid dahlia plates, representing one double and eleven single varieties. Loudon wrote that it was 'the most fashionable flower in this country, and the extent of its cultivation in some of the nurseries . . . is truly astonishing'; by the 1840s there were at least 1,500 named varieties. Competing with the dahlia for the affection of hybridists was the fuchsia, especially after the arrival from Mexico of *F. fulgens* (plate 3801), and most modern hybrids are a cross between this species and *F. magellanica*. Samuel Curtis's garden at Glazenwood prided itself on its display of fuchsia hybrids. The few orchid plates gave a tantalizing glimpse of the treasures waiting to be discovered in the tropical forests on the other side of the Atlantic.

John Sims's first consideration was to present his readers 'with a representation and description of some of the novel and curious plants which are annually introduced, particularly from the Cape of Good Hope'. After the Portuguese sailor, Bartolomeu Dias, rounded the Cape in 1488, it was to become of strategic importance in communication and trade with India and the Far East; by the mid-seventeenth century the Dutch had established a trading post there for reprovisioning their ships. Plants from one of the world's richest floristic regions began to reach Amsterdam; among them was *Kleinia anteuphorbium* (plate 6099) which John Gerard was growing in his London garden in 1596. *Babiana ringens* (plate 6667) was described by Commelinus in 1697 in his *Hortus medicus Amstelodamensis*. Its succulents – aloes, euphorbias, mesembryanthemums and stapelias – and bulbous plants – freesias, gladioli, ixias, galtonias, tritonias and watsonias – were irresistible to plant collectors. When Joseph Banks chose Francis Masson to be Kew's first collector, it was to the Cape that he first sent him. Twenty species of ericas were included in Masson's first consignment and altogether he introduced over 80 species and fostered yet another new fashion in garden flowers. William Curtis built a glasshouse specially for his ericas or Cape heaths at Brompton, and included a catalogue of ericas sold by Richard Williams at his nursery in Turnham Green in his description of *Erica ampullacea* (plate 303). Kew's resident botanical artist, Francis Bauer, drew a selection of

PLATE 9
Nymphaea rubra. Sydenham Edwards. Watercolour. (*Curtis's Botanical Magazine*,
vol. 31, 1810, plate 1280). Introduced soon after 1800 from India where the
seeds are eaten raw or ground into a flour and made into a kind of bread.

Encephalartos longifolius (plate 4903).
Drawn and lithographed by
W. H. Fitch. Collected by
Francis Masson in South Africa in
1775 and still survives in the
Palm House at Kew.

ericas, the finest ever done of the genus, in *Delineations of exotick plants cultivated in the royal garden at Kew* (1796–1803). Henry C. Andrews, with access to the Marquess of Blandford's extensive collection at White Knights, etched 288 plates for his *Coloured engravings of heaths* (1794–1830). Rollisson, a nurseryman at Tooting, had 500 species and varieties which, by careful selection, would provide bloom for every month of the year. Despite their popularity, growers found them difficult plants and in 1874 the *Botanical Magazine* was lamenting that 'no less than 186 species of *Erica* were cultivated at Kew in the year 1811, now we have not above 50' (plate 6108).

Andrews also published an illustrated account of *Geraniums* (1805–*c*.1823) and, selecting from nurserymen's stock, Robert Sweet compiled his *Geraniaceae* in five volumes, 1820–30. The seventh number of the *Botanical Magazine* in 1787 included the first of numerous South African 'geraniums' – *Pelargonium peltatum* (plate 20). Between 1800 and 1826 subscribers to the Magazine were presented with some 500 Cape plants to admire and to covet for their conservatories and glasshouses.

Australian plants got scantier treatment than in the Register and other early nineteenth-century horticultural journals. J. E. Smith whose *Specimens of the botany of New Holland* (1793–95) was the first English survey of the flora of that continent made Australian plants for a while a distinct feature of his *Exotic Botany* (1804–05). Only 48 were delineated in the Magazine in the first decade but there was a reason for this apparent disregard. In 1806 Carl Koenig, joint editor with John Sims of *Annals of Botany* (1804–06) appealed to Sims not to publish any more Australian plants for the time being. Smith was also willing to withhold them from his *Exotic Botany*. This renunciation was in order to give Robert Brown, who had been botanist on Flinders's Australian expedition in 1801, an opportunity to publish his researches on the Australian flora. Sims reluctantly agreed but he was not prepared to delay the publication of some engravings that had already been made. He asked Brown whether he would consider using the *Botanical Magazine* as 'the channel of your communicating observations to the public' if he did not proceed with his book. *Prodromus florae Novae Hollandiae* was eventually published in 1810 and although Brown was preparing another volume he gladly undertook to contribute descriptions to the Magazine. In 1815 the evergreen shrub *Boronia pinnata* (plate 1763) was singled out for commendation: 'on the whole it appears to us to be one of the most desirable plants that have been as yet introduced from New South Wales'. The *Botanical Register* also enjoyed the benefit of Brown's unique knowledge of the Australian flora. In 1839–40 John Lindley, then the editor of the Register published 'A sketch of the vegetation of the Swan River Colony' in Western Australia as part of the *Appendix to the first twenty-three volumes of Edwards's Botanical Register*. By the time Sims retired in 1826, the Magazine had descriptions of over 150 Australian plants to its credit.

Little was known of the flora of China where foreigners were confined from 1755 to the small island of Macao and allowed only to Canton when European ships were in port. Consequently, the only flowers accessible to Europeans stationed there were mainly garden varieties of azaleas, camellias, chrysanthemums and peonies. William Kerr who was in Canton in 1803 sent the tiger lily, *Lilium lancifolium* (plate 1237) to the royal garden at Kew which propagated and distributed over 10,000 bulbs within eight years. *Kerria japonica*, another of his acquisitions, was 'in most of the principal collections about London' (plate 1296) within five years of its introduction in 1805. Seldom an East Indiaman left for England without a portable greenhouse filled with plants selected by John Reeves, the East India Company's tea inspector in Canton. Reeves was also in touch with the Horticultural Society of London, sending them drawings of plants executed by Chinese artists under his supervision. On seeing a painting of *Primula sinensis* (plate 2564), the Society urged Reeves to send plants and seeds without delay.

The Society's first collector, John Potts, went on a round trip to China in 1821, bringing back with him some 40 varieties of chrysanthemums which, unfortunately, were lost on the voyage home. Two years later, John Damper Parks, another of the Society's collectors, was more successful. Returning in 1824 he brought with him 30 varieties of chrysanthemums, a flower which had been grown in Chinese gardens for about 2,000 years. 'The great variety and beauty of these flowers, when cultivated to the perfection of which they are capable, render them a superb acquisition to our gardens', enthused Sims. 'Indeed, till we had seen the magnificent collection of all the varieties hitherto obtained, in the garden belonging to the Horticultural Society, we had formed no idea of the splendid exhibition such an assemblage affords; and that too at a season when our gardens could otherwise boast of but little gaiety' (plate 2556). By 1825 the *Botanical Magazine* had figured three and the *Botanical Register* four of the twenty-seven varieties of chrysanthemums known to be in cultivation in England.

The single red *Camellia japonica* flowered for the first time in England in Lord Petre's garden at Thorndon Hall in Essex in 1739. Little more was heard about it until the 1790s when East Indiamen brought back some new varieties – a double striped and a double white. Samuel Curtis depicted 20 varieties in his *Monograph on the genus Camellia* (1819). One of London's most colourful sights was Alfred Chandler's Camellia House in his nursery at Vauxhall. His son illustrated *Camellia Britannica* (1825) and *Illustrations and descriptions of . . . Camellieae* (1830–37). *Camellia reticulata* (plate 2784), brought back from China in 1820 by Captain Richard Rawes, had double or semi-double flowers and for over a century this cultivated form was the only one known. Then in 1932 J. C. Williams of Caerhays Castle sent Kew specimens of a camellia with single flowers grown from seed collected by George Forrest. What a triumph it must have been for the botanist who identified it as the wild form of *C. reticulata* (plate 9397).

Where did the editor get all these plants for his artists to copy? A regular announcement on the wrappers of the Magazine invited 'Noblemen, Gentlemen and Cultivators in General' with 'new or rare plants' to send them for

Primula sinensis. Left: By John Curtis (plate 2564). It is interesting to compare his portrayal of the plant with that by Matilda Smith.
Right: By Matilda Smith (plate 7559).

[54]

PLATE 10
Salvia barrelieri. No artist is given but possibly Sydenham Edwards. Engraving by
Weddell. (*Curtis's Botanical Magazine*, vol. 43, 1816, plate 1774). Introduced in
1793 from North Africa.

illustration. Many were received unsolicited from friends and gardeners who deemed it a privilege to be represented in the Magazine. Beyond the borders of its commercial centre, much of London was a rural retreat for merchants with their substantial houses and well-tended gardens. The West India merchant, George Hibbert, had a well-stocked garden at Clapham with Joseph Knight as his gardener. Twelve of the plants James Niven collected for him in South Africa, 1798–1802, found their way to Sims and the *Botanical Magazine* which showed its appreciation of his generosity in 1809 by naming *Hibbertia* (plate 1218) in his honour.

William Griffin of South Lambeth, another devotee of the Cape flora, sent 14 South African plants to the Magazine which announced that his 'collection contains more rare and beautiful *Liliaceae* and *Ensetae* [Iridaceae] than all the private collections round London put together' (plate 1618). Fourteen of the South African aloes in the Magazine came from William Curtis's friend, A. H. Haworth.

Robert Barclay, who had encouraged William Curtis to establish his London Botanic Garden, planned his first garden at Clapham. When he moved to Bury Hill in Surrey in 1805 his garden supplied Sims with many subjects including eight plants from North America and six from Australia.

Before William Kent left Clapton for Bath he had sent Sims more than 30 plants from North America, Australia, India and China.

E. J. A. Woodford of Belmont House, Vauxhall was one of Sims's most generous contributors and the flood did not diminish after he had moved to Rickmansworth in Hertfordshire. His total of 80 plants was only surpassed by John Walker of Arnos Grove, Southgate whose offering – over 100 – included 13 Chilean plants.

James Vere of Kensington Gore presented nearly 50 specimens but one wonders whether this was really due to his energetic gardener, William Anderson, since the supply dwindled after Anderson's appointment as Curator of the Chelsea Physic Garden.

Nathaniel Hodson of Lambeth remained loyal to the *Botanical Magazine* after his retirement from the War Office and his removal to Bury St Edmunds where he founded a public botanic garden.

The Comtesse des Vandes's garden at Bayswater with its 'magnificent collection of curious exotica' (plate 1983) was the source of 35 plants, many from South America.[23] Sims allocated two drawings to her *Dahlia* × *hortorum* (plate 1885 a & b) which she had imported from France.

Among the few items from Sir Joseph Banks's wife at Spring Grove, Hounslow was *Rosa arvensis* 'Alba-plena' (plate 1954), collected in China by William Kerr.

One of three Chinese flowers from the 'rare and curious plants' grown by the Rt. Hon. Charles Greville was a tree peony, *Paeonia suffruticosa* (plate 1154). Posterity remembers him as a dilettante and the first lover of Emma Hamilton, but gardeners honour him as one of the founder members of the Horticultural Society of London.

[23] *Gardener's Magazine* thought well enough of her garden to devote an entire article to it (vol. 8, 1832, pp. 476–81).

Nymphaea lotus (plate 797). By Sydenham Edwards. This water-lily flowered at
White Knights, the home of the Marquess of Blandford, in 1803.

Surprisingly, only two plants are acknowledged to Samuel Curtis: a
cardiospermum and a tulip; George Graves had a better record with eight.

The names of quite a few London donors survive only in their solitary gift: for
example, Mr Evans (Stepney), Gabriel Gillett (Drayton Green), John Hall
(Notting Hill), Thomas Wildman (Leyton), Mr Willis (Battersea Rise).

Outside London, A. B. Lambert, Vice-President of the Linnean Society, sent
26 American plants from his estate at Boyton in Wiltshire.

The garden of Sir Abraham and Lady Amelia Hume at Wormleybury in
Hertfordshire was noted for its Chinese plants, but only one, *Paeonia lactiflora*
(plate 1768), was shown in the Magazine.

A wall covered with 22 specimens of *Magnolia grandiflora* was a memorable
sight at White Knights near Reading, an estate which the Marquess of
Blandford (later the Duke of Marlborough) was forced to mortgage as a result of
his extravagant purchases of exotic plants; in 1804 his account with Lee of the
Hammersmith nursery exceeded £15,000. Just four of his acquisitions, however,
got to the *Botanical Magazine*.

Botanic gardens played a minor role as a source of plants. There were
exceptions like the Brompton Botanic Garden, now conducted by Curtis's
partner, William Salisbury, and the Chelsea Physic Garden under its able
Curator, William Anderson.

A few miles to the west of Chelsea was the royal garden at Kew under W. T.
Aiton with Sir Joseph Banks maintaining a vigilant presence. That Sims
received only ten plants from Kew would not have surprised William Herbert
who despised the 'odious and useless establishment'.[24] Herbert deplored 'the

[24] W. Herbert, *Amaryllidaceae*, 1837, p. 247.

[57]

narrow-minded doctrine of Sir Joseph Banks that he could only render the King's collection superior to others by monopolising its contents . . .; if he had freely given and freely received, and made its contents easily accessible to those who were interested in them, it would have been a pleasure and a pride to the nation'. This 'illiberal system' might have been breached if Sims had cultivated W. T. Aiton with the same assiduity as did W. J. Hooker when he became editor. However Sir Joseph Banks lent him drawings of four South African plants for copying in the Magazine.[25]

When Robert Graham took charge of the Botanic Garden at Edinburgh in 1820 a few plants were despatched to Sims, but again, it needed the reputation and persuasion of Hooker after 1826 to turn a trickle into a satisfactory flow.

The decision of seven men meeting in Mr Hatchard's house in Piccadilly on March 7, 1804 to form a 'Society for the Improvement of Horticulture' turned out to be one of the most significant events in the progress of British horticulture. The Horticultural Society of London (subsequently to become the Royal Horticultural Society) rented in 1818 a small plot of ground near Holland House in Kensington for the propagation of the plants they were now acquiring. They had plant collectors in the field from the early 1820s; John Potts and John Parks went to China; George Don joined an Admiralty survey vessel on a tour of the west coast of Africa, the Atlantic seaboard of South America and the West Indies; and John Forbes and James Macrae collected in South America. Their greatest collector during these formative years of the Society was David Douglas who in 1823 made the first of several expeditions to North America.

The temporary garden at Kensington, patently inadequate to accommodate the results of this ambitious collecting policy of the Society, was relinquished in 1821 for 13.5 ha (33 acres) at Chiswick rented from the Duke of Devonshire. Some notion of the variety and range of plants collected, grown and generously distributed by the Society can be gauged from the 28 plants they submitted to the *Botanical Magazine* – from North and South America and the West Indies, South Africa, Mozambique, Sierra Leone, India and China. At its Anniversary Meeting in 1819, celebrating 15 years' satisfactory progress, Fellows were informed that the Society enjoyed 'the most cordial and able assistance from the Nurserymen'.

The spectacular rise of the nursery trade in England was an eighteenth-century phenomenon. At the beginning of the century, Brompton Park, founded in 1681, was the only nursery of any consequence. Its dominant position was soon to be challenged by Thomas Fairchild at Hoxton, Robert Furber at Kensington, and Christopher Gray at Fulham. By the latter half of the century many more competitors had emerged: Daniel Grimwood (Kensington), James Gordon (Mile End), James Lee (Hammersmith), William Malcolm (Kennington), Conrad Loddiges (Hackney), and James Maddock (Walworth). By 1812 London had over 60 seedsmen, nurserymen and florists. Whilst most seedsmen were concentrated in one or two localities such as Fleet Street and Thames Street, the nurserymen found land in the outlying suburbs of Brompton, Chelsea, Hackney and Stockwell. The King's Road in Chelsea was the most

[25] Plates 1276–77, 1283–84.

PLATE 11

Nerium oleander 'Flore-pleno'. No artist is given but possibly Sydenham Edwards.
Engraving by Weddell. (*Curtis's Botanical Magazine*, vol. 43, 1816, plate 1799).
The sweet-scented oleander, native to India and Japan, was introduced to
European gardens in the late seventeenth century.

fashionable area and even those nurserymen with gardens elsewhere in London found it profitable to have a base in the King's Road. By the opening years of Queen Victoria's reign, Sloane Street and both sides of the King's Road were lined with nurseries and their shops. Nurseries occupied about 50 ha (124 acres) of adjacent Kensington.

Throughout its long history the *Botanical Magazine* has been indebted to the nursery trade for many of the plants it has figured and this was particularly so during John Sims's time. It is not too extravagant a claim that without the support of the major nurseries, the Magazine would have experienced some difficulty in obtaining sufficient 'new or rare plants' to fill its monthly numbers. These nurseries include the following establishments.

CONRAD LODDIGES

Dominating the skyline of this famous nursery, founded in Hackney in the 1780s, was a large steam-heated glass palm house, about 24 m (80 ft) long with slender ribs soaring up 12 m (40 ft). It overwhelmed a nurseryman from Frankfurt who saw it in 1829. 'All that I had seen of the kind appeared nothing to me compared with this. I fancied myself in the Brazils; and especially at that moment when Mr. Loddiges had the kindness to produce, in my presence, a shower of artificial rain'.[26] In 1829 its stock of 8,000 species, excluding cultivars, and 2,600 hardy trees and shrubs had an estimated value of £200,000. Well over 200 choice and interesting items were sent to the *Botanical Magazine*. In 1806 John Sims expressed his gratitude by naming a genus – *Loddigesia oxalidifolia* – in honour of Conrad Loddiges. 'So in Loddigesia, the minute white standard may be considered as the emblem of the modest pretensions of this venerable cultivator; and the far-extended wings, as that of his two sons' (plate 965).

LEE AND KENNEDY

Rivalling Loddiges was the Vineyard Nursery at Hammersmith founded in 1745 by James Lee and Lewis Kennedy. The Cape flora was a speciality and just over half of its 80 plants in the Magazine were South African.

CHANDLER AND SONS

According to a Dr Schultes who visited England in 1824, the Vineyard Nursery allocated about half of each working day to the care of their camellia collection. But the largest collection of camellias was kept by Chandler and Sons who, wrote J. C. Loudon with more than a hint of hyperbole, 'may truly be said to have done more for camellias in ten years, than the Chinese have done from the beginning of the world'.[27] Alfred Chandler senior began hybridizing them in 1806. The firm advertised their stock on the wrappers of the *Botanical Magazine* which illustrated two of their varieties of *Camellia japonica*.[28]

[26] *Gardener's Magazine*, vol. 5, 1829, p. 379.
[27] *Ibid*, vol. 7, 1831, p. 349.
[28] Plates 1670 and 2571.

JOHN FRASER

Fraser and his son who collected extensively in North America had a nursery on the corner of Sloane Square about 1786. Their American Nursery, as it was later called, supplied more than 30 plants to the Magazine.

JOSEPH KNIGHT

His Exotic Nursery in the King's Road became a leading supplier of Cape flowers after the purchase of George Hibbert's collection, Knight's former employer. He paid William Baxter £1,500 for the plants and seeds he brought from Australia. Seventy-two of his plants are shown in the Magazine. In 1853, the firm, now Knight and Perry, was purchased by James Veitch.

WHITLEY, BRAMES AND MILNE

This nursery in the Old Brompton Road prided itself on its American novelties and in 1831 still had an enclosure commemorating Mark Catesby, a notable collector of North American plants over a century earlier. The Magazine drew 144 plants received from this firm – from every continent and from islands like the Philippines, Canaries and St Helena.

JAMES COLVILL

This nursery in the King's Road had between 2,800 and 3,700 sq m (30,000 and 40,000 sq ft) under glass. A large greenhouse held between 400 and 500 varieties of *Pelargonium* which Robert Sweet studied for his *Geraniaceae* (1818–20). Just over half of the 25 plants Sims received were from the Cape.

South African flowers were also supplied by Grimwood and Wykes of Kensington and Richard Williams of the Turnham Green Nursery. James and Gwyther in Marylebone and Barr and Brookes in Newington Green – a nursery 'carried on with much spirit, collectors being sent out to distant countries, and many new plants imported' – were frequently acknowledged in the *Botanical Magazine*. After visiting many of these nurseries, Jacob Rinz from Frankfurt solemnly announced that 'there are nowhere else in the world so many large and well kept collections assembled together. To be able merely for once to look at those places would be a sufficient inducement to the Continental gardener to visit England'.[29]

[29] *Gardener's Magazine*, vol. 5, 1829, p. 380.

Loddiges's nursery at Hackney.
(*Journal of Horticulture and Cottage Gardener*, 1896, p. 579).

~ 4 ~

THE HOOKER ERA BEGINS

I N the October 1926 issue of the *Botanical Magazine Potentilla atrosanguinea* (plate 2689) and all the plates for November and December were drawn and described by W. J. Hooker.

William Jackson Hooker was born in Norwich in 1806 and his very early interest in botany, ornithology and entomology pointed the direction in which his future lay. When only twenty-one he was elected a Fellow of the Linnean Society. At the instigation of Sir Joseph Banks he went to Iceland in 1809, but had the misfortune to lose his collections when the ship in which he was returning caught fire and sank. In 1815 he married Maria Sarah, the eldest daughter of Dawson Turner, antiquary, naturalist and banker. In 1816 when the last part of his *British Jungermanniae* came out, he turned his attention to the revision of William Curtis's *Flora Londinensis*, and yet found time to write two books on mosses – *Muscologia Britannia* (1818) and *Musci exotici* (1818–20) – before arriving in Glasgow in 1820 to take up the Chair of Botany. A modest salary, three children and relentless ambition were the spur to further ventures. In August 1822 he embarked upon *Exotic Flora*, a serial publication of 'new, rare, or otherwise interesting exotic plants, especially of such as are deserving of being cultivated in our gardens'. The plants it promoted came from Hooker's own University Botanic Garden at Glasgow and other botanical gardens in the north. J. C. Loudon warmly recommended it, applauding its 'finish and perfection, to which neither the Botanical Magazine nor Register can externally lay claim'.[1] The inadequacy of his university salary coupled with the remoteness of Glasgow from the scientific world centred in London prompted Hooker to

[1] *Gardener's Magazine*, vol. 1, 1826, p. 61.

Sir William Jackson Hooker
(1785–1865) by T. H. Maguire, 1851.
Lithograph.

PLATE 12

Magnolia × thompsoniana. No artist is given. Engraving by Weddell. (*Curtis's Botanical Magazine*, vol. 47, 1820, plate 2164). Probably the first hybrid magnolia in the West, it was raised in the Mile End nursery of Archibald Thompson in 1808.

make discreet enquiries about the possibility of an appointment at the royal garden at Kew. He learnt from Joseph Sabine, Secretary of the Horticultural Society of London, that John Sims was about to retire to Bath and consequently relinquish his editorship of the *Botanical Magazine*. 'If I could once bring myself to believe that Sims was paid £300 a year for conducting the Bot Magazine I would go to London & try to secure to myself that office', he told his father-in-law.[2]

He got his friend, Edward Forster, Treasurer of the Linnean Society, to intercede on his behalf with the Trustees of William Curtis's estate. The future, however, of the Magazine was now precarious. Its sales were being eroded by competition from the *Botanical Register*, *Botanical Cabinet*, *Botanical Garden* and *British Flower Garden*. George Graves had seriously considered but rejected its purchase; the publisher Longmans manifested some interest in it. 'Sabine', Hooker tells Dawson Turner, 'certainly would undertake the publication if I could purchase a share: – which I am really not disposed to do. I have written to him to offer my services as Editor: requiring as remuneration which Dr Sims had received (£100 per annum), & for the drawings £96 per annum: which is really the same as the concern has paid hitherto'.[3] (Obviously Hooker had been misinformed about Sims's salary being £300.)

In the meantime George Graves was negotiating with the publisher, Blackwood, for the purchase of *Exotic Flora*; Hooker consented to staying on as editor provided he was paid the same rate he would have got for editing the *Botanical Magazine*. 'I do not regret having embarked on the Exotic Flora', but, he confided to Turner, 'I shall heartily rejoice to get quit of the present unprofitable side of conducting it'. Hooker was determined to improve both his status and standard of living. He sought the advice of the Duke of Montrose, the patron of Glasgow University, about his future prospects there; he wrote to Ireland about the Chair of Botany at the Dublin Society which had become vacant upon the death of Walter Wade; and he informed Samuel Curtis that he was willing to edit the *Botanical Magazine* for £196 a year.

In July 1826 he was pleased to tell Turner that he was soon to take over the *Botanical Magazine* from Sims and that he would be paid £50 a quarter; furthermore, he had almost finished the first eight plates which would appear in the September or October number; and the *Exotic Flora* would definitely be terminated.

A New Series of the *Botanical Magazine* started in 1827 with Hooker as editor. Couchman was still its printer and Sherwood, Gilbert and Piper published it on behalf of the proprietor, Samuel Curtis. An issue cost 3s.6d. coloured or 3s. plain. The engraver was Joseph Swan of Royal Exchange Square in Glasgow. He had produced the plates in Hooker's *Exotic Flora* and he remained its sole engraver until line-engraving was superseded by lithography in 1845.

A month after his appointment Hooker was complaining to his father-in-law that he had not yet received his first quarter's salary. 'I hope you think the Bot.

[2] Royal Botanic Gardens, Kew. Library (Archives). Sir William Hooker letters, 1805–1832, item 366, December 20, 1825.
[3] *Ibid*, item 368, January 25, 1826.

Lodoicea maldivica (plate 2734).
One of five plates W. J. Hooker gave
to the extraordinary double-coconut
of the Seychelles.

Magazine improved. For the April Nº I have plates of the Suwarrow Nut in all states [plates 2727–28]. For May of the Double Cocoa Nut of the Sechelles [plates 2734–38] which as you know probably grows nowhere in the world but in 3 small islands of a group lying a little to north west of Madagascar: & for June I have the Cactus cochinillifer [plates 2741–42]'.[4] His first few numbers received favourable comment and he informed Turner, who also shared the general approval of the Magazine, that Samuel Curtis wanted to increase the number of plates in each number from eight to twelve.

Hooker who was the sole artist for 1827 and a number of the succeeding years had served a gruelling apprenticeship providing the plates for his father-in-law's *Fuci* (1808–19). His drawing is competent and impeccably accurate for he always had a scientific concern for visual truth. His work in the Magazine was, unfortunately, ill-served by the hand-colouring, decidedly inferior to that provided by Weddell for the preceding volumes.

This first volume of the New Series bears the unmistakable imprint of Hooker: his eclectism (he selected freely from traditional, exotic and economic plants); his refreshing and uninhibited editorial comment (he deplored, for instance, the fact that the Kew collector James Bowie 'in the midst of his usefulness has, by a reckless stretch of parsimony, been recalled' from the Cape (plate 2710)), and, perhaps, above all, his vast web of international correspondents.

The Botanic Garden at Glasgow had only been in existence for about three years when Hooker took charge of it; by 1826 it had in excess of 8,000 species in

[4] *Ibid*, item 338, February 3, 1827.

cultivation, many of which were depicted in the Magazine. He received generous help from his overseas contacts. The Rev. Lansdown Guilding, Chaplain on St Vincent in the West Indies, sent him drawings and specimens of the butter nut, *Caryocar nuciferum* (plates 2727–28), *Opuntia cochinillifera* (plates 2741–42), *Syzygium aromaticum* (plates 2749–50) and *Myristica fragrans* (plates 2756–57); *Solanum montanum* (plate 2768) came from Dr Samuel Mitchill of New York.

Hooker's network of correspondents included many friends and active horticulturists in the British Isles, some of whom contributed to this first volume: Robert Barclay of Bury Hill, Mrs Edward Cropper of Liverpool, Mrs Bewicke of Northumberland, Mrs Arnold Harrison of Aigburgh near Liverpool and W. T. Aiton, Royal Gardener to George IV and director of the royal garden at Kew. Kew's reputation for meanness was the target of frank editorial comment in the *Gardener's Magazine*. 'The difficulty of getting any new plant, cutting or seed from Kew . . . has long been, and still is, a subject of general complaint among gardeners and botanists'.[5] And yet W. J. Hooker through persistence or persuasion won Aiton's co-operation. Thirteen of the plates in 1827 were based on drawings – probably the work of the young Kew gardeners Thomas Duncanson and George Bond – lent by Aiton. It was also Aiton who gave Hooker both specimens and drawings of the cochineal insect (plates 2741–42). 'His patronage and valuable assistance' were acknowledged in the Magazine's dedication in 1828.

Three plates signalled the beginning of a long and productive relationship with Professor Robert Graham at the Botanic Garden in Edinburgh. Twelve plates devoted to orchids were a recognition of their growing popularity and Hooker's fondness for them. *Aster acuminatus* was included with a promise that readers would be introduced to many more species of a genus 'which, flowering in the latest season of autumn constitute the chief ornament of our gardens, till winter comes' (plate 2707).

During his time at Glasgow, Hooker accumulated a varied collection of 'raw and manufactured objects of vegetable origin' which he demonstrated in lectures to his students. When he became Director at Kew this collection formed the nucleus of a museum of economic botany there, the first of its kind in the world. In his first year as editor, Hooker featured the butter nut (plates 2727–28), the clove (plates 2749–50) and the nutmeg (plates 2756–57). John Sims had with some hesitation introduced his readers to a few plants of economic importance such as coffee (plate 1303) and ginger (plate 2000) but Hooker showed no such reluctance. Subsequent volumes of the Magazine included the custard and sugar apple, black pepper, flax, mango, papaw, sandalwood and tea.

His comment to plate 2727 predicted the future trend of the Magazine. 'If we sometimes depart from the rule, to which former editors of the Botanical Magazine appear, rigidly to have adhered, that no plant should be admitted into its pages, except it has been cultivated and brought to blossom in our gardens; it will only be in the rare instances, where, if the plant has been introduced, we have little hope of seeing it produce flowers in this country, or

[5] *Gardener's Magazine*, vol. 2, 1827, p. 315.

PLATE 13

Crataegus laciniata. John Curtis. Watercolour. (*Curtis's Botanical Magazine*, vol. 49, 1822, plate 2314). The fruit was added below this inflorescence in the subsequent engraving.

where the individual is not yet known to our collections, but is most worthy of being cultivated, either from its beauty, or from some useful property residing in it: in both these cases, more will be given but such delineations and descriptions as are taken from living plants, on the fidelity of which we can, with certainty rely'.

Hooker insisted on diagnostic details, essential for the identification of a plant, being added to all drawings. He considered five plants sufficiently important to merit two plates each while the famous double coconut of the Seychelles got five and also ten pages of text. Whenever the occasion demanded it – the *Victoria amazonica*, *Welwitschia mirabilis* or the breadfruit tree – Hooker was generous in his allocation of plates.

This first volume has eight folded plates but Hooker was not too happy about using them, especially as he probably anticipated a greater need for larger plates than did his predecessors. So he initiated a large paper version of the *Botanical Magazine* in 1827. It appears that only six copies, later reduced to three, were produced of the New Series (vols. 54–70 (1827–44)) and possibly only one complete set of the Third Series (vols. 71–130 (1845–1904)).[6] Sir William Thiselton-Dyer who inherited a large paper set from his father-in-law, Sir Joseph Hooker, sold it to H. J. Elwes for £200 in 1906.[7] The Royal Horticultural Society Library bought it from Quaritch in 1948.

[6] *Curtis's Botanical Magazine, index to volumes 1–164*, 1956, p. 253.
[7] F. L. Soper of Lovell Reeve and Company assured Sir William Thiselton-Dyer that his large paper set of vols. 71–130 was unique, the two other sets being incomplete.

Leptospermum flavescens (plate 2695). An early example of floral dissections by W. J. Hooker which subsequently became a regular feature.

The first volume of the Magazine in 1787 carried a dedication to Mrs Montagu Burgoyne, 'admired for the Accuracy with which she paints the Beauties of Flora'. William Curtis, however, neglected to maintain the practice and it was Hooker who resurrected it by appropriately dedicating his first volume to Robert Barclay, recollecting that 'upwards of Forty Years ago, the First Series of the Botanical Magazine was begun, under your auspices, by its lamented Editor, Mr William Curtis'.

Two plates of *Adansonia digitata* made a splendid beginning to the volume for 1828. The Baobab tree, one of the largest and longest-lived trees in the world, has been called 'the oldest organic monument of our planet'. A native of West Africa, it has been successfully introduced into many tropical countries. Hooker based his plates on Indian drawings lent to him by General Hardwicke and specimens of the flowers and fruit sent from St Vincent by the Rev. L. Guilding. The reader learns that natives in East Africa hollow out chambers in the trunks 'and within them are suspended the dead bodies of those who are refused the honor of burial. There they become mummies, perfectly dry and well preserved, without any further preparation or embalment' (plates 2791–92). Hooker frequently enhanced his taxonomic notes with snippets of history, folklore and ethnobotany. Incidental information such as the use of the globe amaranth as garlands to adorn the hair or as decoration for musical instruments introduced an element of readability that the Magazine never had before.

After clothes nothing is possibly more susceptible to the whims of fashion than horticulture. Tulipomania was an extreme manifestation of public passion. Orchids became a Victorian status symbol. The ferns, ignored for so long, were suddenly collected with fanatical fervour. Pteridomania revolved largely around European species suitable for fern gardens and glass cases in the house. W. J. Hooker was the leading pteridologist of his day and the Wedgwood memorial plaque to him in Kew Church is decorated with ferns to commemorate his life-long interest. So it was to be expected that he would find it irresistible to slip one into the Magazine. He enthusiastically recommended *Blechnum fraxineum* (plate 2818) as 'a striking and beautiful feature' for the conservatory.

Hooker was a compulsive editor. In 1829, just two years after he had taken on the *Botanical Magazine*, he founded the *Botanical Miscellany* for plants which 'recommend themselves by their novelty, rarity or history'. But this extra burden in no way impaired the smooth management of the Magazine. A letter from one satisfied subscriber was published in the often censorious *Gardener's Magazine*. 'The plates of Curtis's *Magazine*, as now published, may be held up as the most correct and beautiful portraits of plants that have ever been published at the price: and every one acquainted with botanical subjects fully appreciates the talents which Dr. Hooker shows in the description'.[8] And when a rival, the *Horticultural Register* admitted that 'the many intelligent remarks of the Editor always make this Work doubly interesting',[9] Samuel Curtis must have congratulated himself on his discernment in appointing Hooker as editor.

[8] *Gentleman's Magazine*, vol. 6, 1830, p. 499.
[9] *Horticultural Register*, October 1831, p. 212.

PLATE 14

Gladiolus delenii. Sir William Hooker. Watercolour. (*Curtis's Botanical Magazine,*
vol. 57, 1830, plate 3032). The note at the top of the drawing is addressed to
Mr Graves who was responsible for the colouring of the plates.

But after the initial honeymoon, it was not long before relations between the two men became strained and tense. In some distress Hooker told Turner that he had heard that Curtis proposed living in Constantinople for five years, transferring his business from Walworth to Glazenwood where his daughters would conduct it during his absence. If that happened, Hooker forecast that the payment of his quarterly salary would become even more erratic than it was at present. 'Curtis is not a fit publisher for the Magazine', expostulated Hooker.[10] 'Every letter I have is full of complaints of the sales being worse & worse: so that unless it gets into better hands I cannot conceive that it can continue to yield a return for the expenses upon it.' He appealed to Turner to ask J. and J. Arch, one of its distributors, whether they knew Curtis's plans. 'I should be concerned beyond measure if I was to lose the Authorship of that [Magazine] & its consequent remuneration of £200 for I hope & believe that it adds to my credit as well as to my income'. Hooker was greatly relieved to learn that Curtis was unlikely to go to Constantinople. He admitted to his father-in-law that he was aware that 'an opinion prevails that I do not make the Magazine sufficiently popular',[11] and that Turner thought he should include more of the popular common flowers in British gardens. At the same time Curtis was pressing him for more 'new & showy' plants but it was impossible to satisfy all these demands, especially when subscribers also expected him to figure their submissions.

In 1831 Samuel Curtis finally moved from Walworth, his birthplace and home for so many years, to conduct his business from his country residence and nursery at Glazenwood. In a small pamphlet[12] on Glazenwood he revealed that only four complete sets of the old series up to 1826 of the Magazine were still available for purchase. He was giving a great deal of thought to its future and the omens alarmed Hooker. 'Curtis seemed determined to alter the character of the Magazine & to employ another Editor', he confided to Turner.[13] Robert Graham at Edinburgh had already warned Curtis that such a step would lose him public support. Hooker sought his father-in-law's intervention in this deteriorating relationship. Curtis had assured Hooker that he did not doubt his diligence. 'All I have ever complained of is the poor miserable subjects which are selected to be the figures represented, whilst so many ornamental plants do not find access & which are now getting into common cultivation'. Hooker begged Turner for any suggestions to improve the Magazine, reminding him that 'I have been especially careful to follow your advice, so often given, of introducing economical & useful plants, & have entered much at large into their history & have even put myself to great expense in procuring subjects of this kind'. Samuel Curtis had calculated he was losing £100 a year on the *Botanical Magazine* and

[10] Royal Botanic Gardens, Kew. Library (Archives). Sir William Hooker letters, 1805–1832, item 437, March 7, 1830.

[11] *Ibid*, item 439, April 4, 1830.

[12] *An address to the public, more particularly to those of the nobility and gentry who patronize horticulture; also, to the immediate patrons, friends and visitors of Glazenwood, near Coggeshall in the County of Essex*, 1831 (The William Curtis Museum at Alton has a copy of this rare publication).

[13] Royal Botanic Gardens, Kew. Library (Archives). Sir William Hooker letters, 1805–1832, item 466, May 27, 1832.

Hooker feared he was preparing to take over the editorship himself. At least that was the interpretation Hooker put on the following statement from Curtis. 'I hope by your knowing it so long before hand you will only provide for the plates of the present volume & I will get some ready for the next if I think it safe to go on with it'.

Badgered by his son-in-law's importunity, the long-suffering Turner dutifully wrote to Curtis extolling Hooker's editorial capabilities. Hooker thanked him effusively and rewarded him by unburdening, at inordinate length, all his fears and difficulties.[14] Curtis, it seems, believed it was essential for the editor to live in London near the large concentration of gardens and nurseries. Hooker, while conceding that this was not an unreasonable requirement, had repeatedly requested Curtis in vain to send plants from Glazenwood and the London nurseries to Glasgow. Hooker reminded Curtis that certain plants he wanted to see in the Magazine were not available in the north. The *Botanical Register* was held up as a model for Hooker to emulate. The unkindest cut was the rumour put about by some of Curtis's friends that Hooker was 'paid by the Register to render the Magazine as little ornamental & useful as possible'. 'It is quite untrue that I *prefer* the lesser to the more ornamental, I always give the preference to the most beautiful when I can obtain them but situated as I am, that is not always possible.'

Hooker was confident that if he lost his post as editor, the 'Scotch subscribers will almost to a man give up the work . . . . I was assured by old Graves that I brought an accession of 400 subscribers to this work (he told me there was a demand for 1,200 copies). Eight hundred copies a month independent of back numbers, & sets sold from time to time ought to pay'. He begged his father-in-law to intercede on his behalf once more.

With obvious relief, just over a month later, he told Turner that he was to remain editor.[15] 'Indeed I have good reason to believe that he heartily repented of giving me warning to discontinue my labours & that he already found that Don[16] was not the man (however good a Botanist) to give popularity to the work'. Hooker again advanced the opinion he firmly held that the price of the Magazine should be increased to 4s. Maria Hooker informed her father that Curtis had agreed to continue the Magazine for a few more years 'to see if it can be made rather more showy'.[17]

In the volume for 1832 there is no hint of the tension behind the scenes: orchids and economic plants proliferated, many novelties were coming from the Botanic Garden at Edinburgh, and Australian plants collected by Allan Cunningham were forwarded by Aiton at Kew. Curtis with his liking for the ostentatious almost certainly disapproved of the inclusion of *Prunus myrtifolia* notwithstanding his editor's justification. 'No living plant, however, has come under my close

---

[14] Royal Botanic Gardens, Kew. Library (Archives), Sir William Hooker letters, 1805–1832, item 469, August 7, 1832.

[15] *Ibid*, item 472, September 19, 1832.

[16] Presumably David Don (1799–1841), Librarian of the Linnean Society, who was a frequent contributor to the *British Flower Garden*.

[17] Letter in private possession. October 18, 1832.

observation: nor should I have deemed it deserving of being figured in the *Botanical Magazine*, under these circumstances, slight as are its pretensions on the score of beauty, were it not a plant of which no satisfactory figure exists, and which may at the same time be reckoned an economical one' (plate 3141). Conscious of the absence of many common garden favourites, Hooker drew the hollyhock and the marigold in his own garden.[18] From time to time he found room for other familiar flowers like the nasturtium, a 'great favourite with the humble cottager' (plate 3375).

When the second edition of James Sowerby's *English Botany* (1832–1846) arranged its plates in systematic order, partly coloured, and with shorter descriptions, it prompted Samuel Curtis to do likewise with the old series of the *Botanical Magazine*. As long ago as 1815 when general indexes to the first 42 volumes were published, John Sims had recommended binding the plates in a systematic arrangement complemented by the letter press in a numerical sequence. The first number of the second edition of the *Botanical Magazine* appeared on April 1, 1833 with four plates, 1s. partly coloured or 2s. fully coloured. The arrangement of the plates followed the natural system formulated in De Candolle's *Prodromus*. Hooker supplied the descriptions and Curtis the cultivation notes. The *Gardener's Magazine* welcomed it as 'a great service' and some years later proposed the sale of loose plates from the Magazine, the *Register* and other illustrated works so that botanists and gardeners could merge them into one systematic sequence.[19] Hooker told Turner that 'to aid poor Curtis, I have undertaken to publish the new Edition free of cost, to him'[20] but only one volume, comprising 119 plates, of this classified arrangement of the earlier parts was ever published.

Although Hooker was an unashamed workaholic, he gladly accepted drawings from members of the Curtis family, from J. D. C. Sowerby, James McNab and Dr Greville at Edinburgh and others to ease his task of having to

[18] Plates 3198 and 3204.
[19] *Gardener's Magazine*, vol. 12, 1836, p. 153.
[20] Royal Botanic Gardens, Kew. Library (Archives). Sir William Hooker letters, 1805–1832, item 7, June 8, 1833.

Walter Hood Fitch (1817–1892).

provide most of the illustrations for the Magazine. Hooker was extremely relieved to be able to employ a young botanical artist he had trained. Walter Hood Fitch, born in Glasgow in 1817, the son of a clerk, had been an apprenticed pattern-drawer in a calico mill. His artistic talent so impressed Hooker that he taught him the rudiments of botanical drawing. Hooker writes of him enthusiastically to Turner. 'I have left at home a most industrious young artist who is assisting me in getting up a valuable set of drawings for the use of my Class'.[21] Hooker obtained his release from his apprenticeship and was pleased with the progress he continued to make. 'I cannot make of him a *theoretical* Botanist, but he has so good an eye & so much sound sense that he is of more use to me than many a professed Botanist would be. He is becoming a most beautiful artist. He executes lithographs admirably'. Furthermore Fitch's deft floral analyses fulfilled Hooker's rigorous requirements. His first signed plate in the *Botanical Magazine – Mimulus lewisii* (plate 3353) – appeared in the October 1834 number. All the unsigned plates in that year and the following one were his work,[22] and before long the Magazine was to depend exclusively on Fitch for over 40 years.

Occasionally Hooker would enliven his descriptions with pertinent extracts from the letters of his many correspondents: a collector in the field, a curator of a colonial botanical garden or an expatriate in the tropics with an interest in the local flora. Their communications or observations were quoted much more extensively in his *Journal of Botany* (the continuation of his *Botanical Miscellany*). From August 1835 two sheets of separately paginated letterpress and two partly-coloured plates, added to each issue of the *Botanical Magazine*, were devoted to interesting news which did not fall within the prescribed limits of the Magazine. This *Companion to the Botanical Magazine* cost 1s.6d. as a separate issue or 1s. if stitched with the monthly number. The first article was from a 'Journal of an ascent to the summit of Adam's Peak, Ceylon' by Colonel and Mrs Walker. Other articles such as T. Drummond's collecting in the U.S.A., Colonel Hall's in Ecuador and R. Gunn's and T. Scott's in Tasmania were continued from the *Journal of Botany* – a peculiar arrangement. The *Companion* lasted only until 1837, but as late as 1839 the *Gardener's Magazine* still lamented its demise.

Although honoured by a Hanoverian knighthood in 1836, awarded for his outstanding services to botany, Hooker was still troubled by the uncertain future of the *Botanical Magazine*. In 1837 Curtis was negotiating its purchase by Longmans, the publisher of Hooker's *Journal of Botany*, but Curtis's valuation of the copyright was a stumbling block. The possibility of its distributor, Sherwood, acting as agent for the Magazine until Curtis could dispose of it was anathema to Hooker. Curtis urged Hooker to prepare a 'showy number' for January 1838, presumably to impress any potential purchasers.[23] Curtis's financial difficulties constantly delayed the payment of Hooker's quarterly

[21] Royal Botanic Gardens, Kew. Library (Archives). Sir William Hooker letters, 1805–1832, item 24, May 31, 1834.
[22] W. Botting Hemsley, *A new and complete index to the Botanical Magazine*, 1906, p. xxxv.
[23] Royal Botanic Gardens, Kew. Library (Archives). Sir William Hooker letters, 1805–1832, item 72, October 24, 1837 to Turner.

salary. 'I sometimes doubt whether I had not better offer to supply the materials for the Mag^e for £50 a year less than I have hitherto received, rather than it should come to close'.[24]

In January 1838 Curtis announced changes in the *Botanical Magazine*.[25] In February he revealed that he 'was not aware that the Botanical Register was about to adopt a plan so precisely similar to that which he there proposed'.[26] He was therefore undecided whether he should make the proposed alterations. The disastrous effects of competition were admitted. 'That the supply of these Works [i.e. other periodicals] has greatly exceeded the demand there can be no question, when it is known that three of them have ceased to exist; and, that one, which alone is worthy of being looked upon in the light of a fair and honorable competitor (the Botanical Register) has adopted a considerable alteration to its plan. That such a number of competitors should injure the sale of the Botanical Magazine was to be expected, and has, indeed, caused a considerable loss to its Proprietor'. Nevertheless, Curtis affirmed his intention to continue the Magazine 'with increased vigour' and promised that the 'Plates shall increase in beauty, and the Descriptions exceed in interest, those of any of the preceding volumes'.

1838 was a critical year not only for the *Botanical Magazine* and the *Botanical Register* but also for the royal garden at Kew. An official investigation of royal expenditure which followed the accession of Queen Victoria in 1837 included in its purview all the royal gardens. John Lindley, Professor of Botany at University College London and Secretary of the Horticultural Society of London, was nominated to report on the royal gardens, assisted by 'two or more practical Gardiners' (Joseph Paxton, gardener to the Duke of Devonshire and John Wilson, gardener to the Earl of Surrey). The botanic garden at Kew was to receive close scrutiny. The trio made harsh comments on the management of the Kew garden: lack of space, overcrowded glasshouses, no systematic arrangement of plants and inadequate labelling. Their report[27] observed that 'there are many gardens in the British colonies and dependencies . . . [but] their utility is much diminished by the want of some system under which they can be regulated and controlled . . . . A National Botanic Garden would be the centre around which all these lesser establishments should be arranged . . . . Such a garden would be the great source of new and valuable plants to be introduced and dispersed throughout this country'. Kew could rightly assume this role of a National Botanic Garden, 'gradually made worthy of the country, and converted into a powerful means of promoting national science, or should be abandoned'. For various reasons the Government did not finally decide the future of Kew until 1840 when it was transferred from the Lord Steward's Department to the Commissioners of Woods and Forests, a step originally proposed in Lindley's report.

This transfer of Kew to the Commissioners of Woods and Forests raised Hooker's expectations which he disclosed in a letter to Lindley in August 1840.

---

[24] *Ibid*, item 74, November 10, 1837 to Turner.
[25] This was printed on the wrapper and, unfortunately, no copy of it has yet been traced.
[26] Wrapper, February 1838.
[27] Royal Botanic Gardens, Kew. Copy in the Kewensia collection in the Library.

'Like you I have heard *rumours* of my appointment, but if such has taken, or even *is* to take place, I *know* nothing of it. I am in the same position in having me fixed at Kew in the event of a change taking place in the Curatorship; and, ever since, there have been highly influential people who are anxious and who are as I believe exerting themselves on my behalf'. In March 1841 Hooker's anxieties about his future were put to rest when he was offered the post of Director of the small botanic garden of 4.5 ha (11 acres) at Kew, the adjacent pleasure grounds remaining the responsibility of the aged Aiton. Two months later he, his family and Fitch were installed at Kew. John Lindley apart, Sir William Hooker was unquestionably the best qualified candidate for the post. He was a distinguished botanist enjoying an international reputation, the author of many botanical works, the owner of an exceptional herbarium and library, and with 20 years' experience in running the University Botanic Garden at Glasgow. His age – fifty-six – was his only conceivable disadvantage, but he set about the daunting task of creating a national botanical garden with the enthusiasm and energy of a much younger man.

His salary – £300 a year and another £200 in lieu of a house – eased his perpetual financial crises but he still worried about the *Botanical Magazine*. 'Out of the income from the Bot. Mag^e [of £160 a year] I may reckon I have to pay Fitch £100 a year'[28] for drawing for the Magazine and other works. Samuel Curtis had removed himself to Rozel in Jersey and, according to Hooker, took no interest whatsoever in the Magazine. Both he and the engraver, Swan, had not been paid. His only consolation was the realization that 'bad as it pays I quite believe it pays as well if not better than any of the kind. *All* have died away except the Register & this'.[29]

On being reassured by the Curtis family that outstanding debts to the distributor, Sherwood, would be cleared and that he himself would be paid regularly every two months, Hooker agreed to remain editor. 'I fear the whole family of the Curtis have gone wrong – the Father has long been without a shilling I believe of his own: – the son, who has the Nursery, has let the house & lives in a cottage & Miss Curtis takes up her abode with another brother in Staines. She is consequently unable to fold & stitch the numbers as heretofore & that was, I believe, her main support & I have good reason to think that all the proceeds of her work are now made over to Sherwood'.[30] Sherwood was now, in effect, the Magazine's controller and manager, paying bills as and when he could or pleased. Hooker with the resources of the Royal Botanic Gardens at Kew now at his disposal pondered promoting a journal similar to the *Botanical Magazine* with a title such as *Kew Gardens* or *Plants of Kew*. By 1844 sales had dropped to 400 copies and bankruptcy seemed inevitable. Swan threatened legal action to get the money due to him; other creditors including Hooker announced they could no longer work for the Magazine beyond March 1845.[31]

[28] Royal Botanic Gardens, Kew. Library (Archives). Sir William Hooker letters, 1833–1844, item 353, November 13, 1841, to Turner.
[29] *Ibid*, item 372, March 14, 1842, to Turner.
[30] *Ibid*, item 532, July 31, 1844 to Turner.
[31] *Ibid*, Sir William Hooker letters 1845–1851, item 7, February 7, 1845.

Hooker felt himself 'at liberty to seek out for a publication for myself. But where to go is the thing & how to hook it on to the present work so as to keep up the present subscribers'. Through family loyalty, wilful stubbornness or lingering hope the Curtis family 'cling to the Magazine, & will not give it up: though they cannot afford to conduct it'.[32] Then, almost miraculously, a publisher appeared, willing to take the risk of attempting to restore its foundering fortunes. Lovell Reeve who had been in protracted negotiations with the Curtis family finally committed himself when it was rumoured that the *Botanical Register*, the only serious rival, was to cease at the end of the year. So confident was Reeve of his ability to rescue the Magazine that he readily agreed to all Curtis's demands, including the presentation of 30 or 40 copies of the Magazine to the family for the next five years. He also promised to advertise the earlier series on behalf of the Curtis family who had retained the old stock.[33] Also, Sir William Hooker was to remain editor.

An analysis of the sources of the plants figured in the *Botanical Magazine* from 1827 to 1844 validate Sir William Hooker's repeated complaints that he received little or no help from Samuel Curtis. Only 14 plants are recorded as having come from Curtis's own garden and nursery at Glazenwood. The stock of the nurseries which had been the mainstay of Sims dwindled to the occasional offering. Those in the south of England, remote from Hooker in Glasgow, are represented by three plants from Knight of Chelsea, one from Chandler in Vauxhall, two from the Epsom Nursery, one from James Veitch at Exeter and ten cacti from Fred Mackie of the Lakenham Nursery near Ipswich. But Hooker did not do much better nearer home – just token gifts from the Comley Bank Nursery and Dickson and Company at Edinburgh, the Monkwood Nursery at Ayr and Mr Sangton of Kirkaldy.

Sir William fared rather better with individual owners of gardens. His most generous contributor was the Sixth Duke of Bedford to whom he dedicated the 1831 volume of the Magazine. His estate at Woburn Abbey supplied 39 specimens, principally from Central and South America. Fifteen plants were selected from the gardens at Wentworth House, the home of Viscount Milton. Also, Hooker could always depend on Robert Barclay (Bury Hill), Mrs Beaumont (Bretton Hall) and James Bateman (Knypersley) for interesting flowers but his main source was the botanic gardens.

First and foremost, inevitably, was his own Botanic Garden at Glasgow; over 300 plants came from its collections. A steady stream, amounting to just over 250 items (the New World and Australia predominantly) came from the Botanic Garden at Edinburgh with its keeper, Robert Graham, writing most of the descriptive notes and his Curator, William McNab, drawing 28 of the plates. Nearly 100 plants or drawings were acknowledged to Aiton at Kew; after his appointment as Director there in 1841, Hooker lost no time utilizing its collections. The botanical gardens at Belfast, Dublin, Liverpool and the new one at Birmingham also helped.

---

[32] *Ibid*, item 17, February 20, 1845.
[33] Vols. 68 to 70 (1841–44) are relatively rare as the Curtis family sold them as waste paper. (W. Botting Hemsley, *A new and complete index to the Botanical Magazine*, 1906, p. xxxviii).

David Douglas (1799–1834).

The flora of the New World dominated the *Botanical Magazine* during Hooker's editorship under Curtis. Over 60 plants from the West Indies were described and nearly 190 from North America, the latter largely the harvest of two collectors, David Douglas and Thomas Drummond.

David Douglas (1799–1834) was engaged as a gardener at the Botanic Garden at Glasgow about the same time as Hooker took up his appointment as Professor of Botany there. Douglas attended his lectures, the two men became acquainted and when the Horticultural Society of London was seeking a plant collector in 1823, Hooker recommended him for the post. In his memoir of Douglas, Hooker recalled that 'his great activity, undaunted courage, singular abstemiousness and energetic zeal, at once pointed him out as an individual eminently calculated to do himself credit as a scientific traveller'.[34] Douglas made several expeditions to North America on behalf of the Horticultural Society, crossing the continent to the Pacific seaboard. Hooker frequently acknowledged the valuable contributions of his protegé. 'The beautiful Genus of Lupinus . . . has been greatly increased by the discoveries of Mr Douglas on the north-west coast of America, where that indefatigable Naturalist has detected no less than seventeen species on his first visit to the shores of the Columbia, and several have rewarded him on his second visit' (plate 3283). Three species of Penstemon were described in 1829. 'The recent travels of Mr Douglas and Mr Drummond among the Rocky Mountains, and in the north-west part of America, have been the means of enriching our gardens with many highly beneficial species of the Genus Penstemon' (plate 2954). Of the 14 species and varieties of the ornamental currant, *Ribes sanguineum* was without doubt the most popular. The Horticultural Society thought it alone justified the expense of Douglas's three-year expedition and Hooker commented: 'Few, if any of the numerous interesting and hardy plants, introduced to our gardens by Mr. Douglas . . . are more truly deserving of cultivation and of a place in our Gardens and in our shrubberies than the subject of the present plate [3335]'.

Twelve of the 19 plants the Horticultural Society chose from their garden at Chiswick for the *Botanical Magazine* were Drummond introductions. Douglas

[34] *Companion to the Botanical Magazine*, vol. 2, 1836, pp. 78–182.

3138.

W.J.H.del.^t   Pub by S.Curtis Glazenwood Essex Mar 1.1832   Swan Sc

PLATE 15
Lobelia assurgens var. *portoricensis*. William Jackson Hooker. Engraving by
J. Swan. (*Curtis's Botanical Magazine*, vol. 19, 1832, plate 3138).

who had known Thomas Drummond in Scotland, met him again in North America in 1827 when he was an assistant naturalist on Sir John Franklin's Arctic expedition. The Glasgow and Edinburgh Botanic Gardens and several private subscribers paid the expense of his return to North America in 1831 and Hooker distributed his collections. When he died in Havana in 1835, Hooker named *Phlox drummondii* (plate 3441), one of his last introductions, in memory of 'its unfortunate discoverer'.

New World plants had been grown in European gardens ever since the days of the early colonists. But the Spanish and Portuguese prohibited or hindered unauthorized access to their possessions in Central and South America and it was not until the nineteenth century when such restrictions were relaxed that British collectors were able to explore its forests and savannahs. From 1824 to 1826 James Macrae collected in Brazil, Peru and Chile for the Horticultural Society which, in 1836, sent one of its clerks, Theodore Hartweg, to Mexico.

Sir William Hooker suggested to one of his medical students, George Gardner, that he went to Brazil, a country relatively little known, whose flora had been briefly sampled by Cunningham, Bowie and Burchell. Gardner arrived at Rio de Janeiro in 1836 and made the Organ Mountains, some 60 miles north of the city, a base for his collecting. He was overwhelmed by the luxuriance of the vegetation. 'Pretty herbaceous ferns and handsome-flowered *Begonias* were trodden down at every footstep. The stems of the large trees were covered with *Bromelias*, *Tillandsias*, Orchideae, ferns . . ., a pretty *Fuchsia*, in full flower was trailing over the bare rocks, in their clefts grew a handsome *Amaryllis*'.[35] The extraordinary diversity of the flora of this particular range of mountains

[35] G. Gardner, *Travels in the interior of Brazil*, edn. 2, 1849.

A view of the Organ Mountains in Brazil. (G. Gardner, *Travels in the interior of Brazil principally through the northern provinces*, second edition, 1849, frontispiece).

attracted other collectors like the Veitch employee, William Lobb. 'It is, indeed, a remarkable fact, and an evidence of the great variety of the Brazilian vegetation, that, although Mr Lobb and Mr Gardner were botanizing in the same range of mountains at the same time, each met with plants the other did not find' (plate 4170). One of the plants he collected, *Prepusa hookeriana*, Gardner dedicated to Hooker 'as the most lasting memento I can offer him for his first suggesting my voyage to Brazil' (plate 3907).

Mrs Arnold Harrison of Aigburgh near Liverpool gave the *Botanical Magazine* 15 Brazilian plants. She and Richard Harrison had an outstanding collection of plants from that country. 'Their connection with Rio Janeiro, and the circumstances of their having a near relative resident there, who loses no opportunity of collecting the vegetable treasures of that country for them, have been the means of their introducing to Britain some of the choicest productions now existing in our stoves' (plate 2755).

Some of the orchids George Skinner collected for James Bateman in Guatemala appeared in the *Botanical Magazine*. Two notable orchid growers, Charles Horsfall of Everton and John Moss of Otterspool, also sent Hooker some of their American specimens.

One of Hooker's numerous correspondents was John Tweedie who had emigrated to Argentina in 1825. Hooker published 15 of his Argentinian plants, several from Brazil and one from Uruguay.

Another British resident in Argentina was Dr John Gillies who 'supplied the Glasgow and other Botanic Gardens with no less than twenty-two species [of cacti]; all gathered within the distance of a morning's ride [from Mendoza]' (plate 3107). Dr Graham wrote that 'an entirely new aspect has been given to our greenhouses within these few years, by the kindness of Dr Gillies and Mr Cruickshanks, particularly in most interesting additions from genera Fuchsia, Calceolaria, Salpiglossis, Schizanthus and Loasa' (plate 2874).

After a period of neglect, cacti came into fashion during the 1830s with collectors such as the Dukes of Bedford and Devonshire, Mr Harris at Kingsbury, the Rev. Williams at Hendon, and A. B. Lambert whose collection of *Opuntia* at Boyton was presented to Kew in 1841. The acquisition of Thomas Hitchin's collection made Mackie's Lakenham Nursery the foremost grower and supplier of cacti. Prices ranging between 10 and 30 guineas were not infrequently paid for just one coveted *Echinocactus*.

About 50 of the plants (or drawings) the *Botanical Magazine* received from W. T. Aiton at Kew came from the Australian colony. Kew sent one of its employees, Allan Cunningham, to New South Wales in 1816 where he collected seeds and herbarium specimens for the next 15 years. William Baxter who worked in Western Australia for John Mackay in 1823 made his employer's Clapton Nursery well-known for its Australian plants. Thomas Drummond's brother, James, became superintendent of a new botanical garden in Western Australia in 1829 and corresponded with Sir William Hooker who published his letters in his *Journal of Botany* and its sequel over a period of 14 years. Charles Fraser became Colonial Botanist in New South Wales in 1821, five years after his arrival there. Almost 200 of the plants raised in Great Britain from these

Cereus chalybaeus (plate 3922). W. H. Fitch. Engraved by J. Swan.
'Every year, I might almost say, every month, brings to light new forms among
this singular race. Perhaps no limited portion of the New World can exhibit to the
eye such assemblages of Cacteae as are now to be met with in many
collections in England and on the continent' – W. J. Hooker in 1842.

collections were featured in the *Botanical Magazine* from 1827 to 1844. Allan
Cunningham headed the list, sometimes adding notes on the Australian flora.[36]
Hibiscus splendens with its profusion of delicate pink and crimson flowers, was
rated by the Magazine in 1830 as 'the king of all the known Australian plants'
(plate 3025).

Sir William Hooker who exchanged plants and seeds with Carl F. Heinrich
von Ludwig in the Cape Colony dedicated vol. 62 to him. But fewer than 50
plants from Ludwig and other South African correspondents were drawn for the
Magazine during this period. Sir William regretted the continuing loss
of Cape plants from British gardens. At one time, he reminded his readers,
gardens and nurseries 'could boast of many choice specimens of Cape
Proteaceous plants, which, in the present day, are nowhere to be seen; for having
been urged by culture to put forth their showy flowers, they immediately
afterwards, in many instances, exhibited, from some mistreatment, debilities
and sickness, and eventually dying, have ever since been lost to Britain' (plate
3500).

[36] e.g. plates 3251 and 3272.

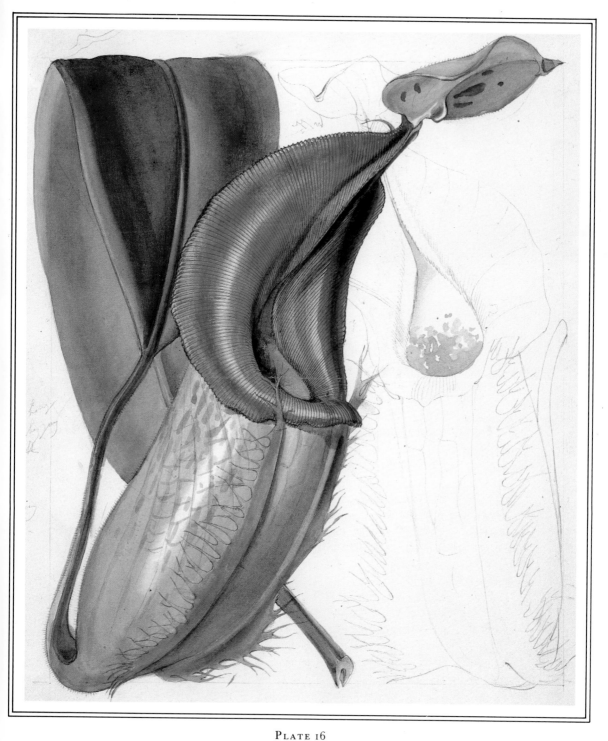

PLATE 16

Nepenthes veitchii. W. H. Fitch. Watercolour. (*Curtis's Botanical Magazine*, vol. 84, 1858, plate 5080). This insectivorous plant was collected by Thomas Lobb for the Veitch nursery in the late 1840s in Sarawak.

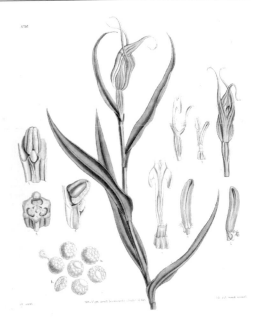

Pterostylis banksii (plate 3172).
Francis Bauer. Engraved by J. Swan.
Note the pollen grains in
right-hand corner.
~~left~~

Sir William was, as has been already mentioned, never reluctant to supplement his supply of living material with accurate drawings. They came from Aiton, Niven, Mackie, Mrs Harrison, Mrs Telfair, Samuel Curtis's large family and his friend Clara Pope, Dr Greville, the ever faithful and industrious Rev. William Herbert and Mrs Withers, flower painter to Queen Adelaide. His most distinguished artist was Francis Bauer at Kew. His meticulous drawing of *Pterostylis banksii* (plate 3172) demonstrates his remarkable skill with a microscope. He informed Hooker that he had 'examined the Pollen Grains with Ploessel's grand microscope, and, to my great surprise, found a total deviation from those of all the hundreds of specimens of Orchidaceous plants I have yet investigated . . . . These I consider an important circumstance, and could not be detected by Botanists possessed only of glasses of moderate power'.

Vignette of Palm House at Kew.
(On wrapper of *Curtis's Botanical Magazine*, January, 1845).

[84]

❧ 5 ❧

LOVELL REEVE
TAKES OVER

L OVELL Reeve (1814–1865), who had so boldly – and perhaps even rashly – purchased the *Botanical Magazine* from Samuel Curtis, could be considered the leading natural history publisher of the nineteenth century – 'one of the most eminent scientific publishers this country has produced' was the opinion of *The Bookseller*.[1] Reeve's devotion to natural history evolved from earnest shell collecting as a boy; shells provided the subject of his first major work, *Conchologia systematica* (1840–41). With the modest profits derived from a sale of his shells, Reeve opened a shop in King William Street in the Strand in 1843 for the sale of natural history specimens and the publication of conchological books. Equipped with Stanhope and lithographic presses, he embarked on his most ambitious book, *Conchologia iconica*. Under the imprint of Reeve Brothers, he began publishing in 1844 the first number of Joseph D. Hooker's classic work, *The botany of the Antarctic voyage*. Sir William Hooker's *London Journal of Botany* (a continuation of *Journal of Botany*) was taken over by Reeve, Benham and Reeve in the same year.

While Lovell Reeve was contemplating making an offer for the *Botanical Magazine*, Samuel Curtis and Sir William Hooker launched the Third Series with the January number for 1845. Its new sub-title defined its limits: 'the plants of the Royal Gardens of Kew, and of other botanical establishments in Great Britain'. A wood-engraved vignette of the new Palm House, now under construction, stressed the close links of the Magazine with Kew. The *Companion to*

---

[1] *Bookseller*, December 30, 1865.

Lovell Reeve (1814–1865)
by T. H. Maguire, 1849. Lithograph.

the Botanical Magazine was resurrected in a new series to provide 'a supplement of botanical and horticultural information'.

When Lovell Reeve assumed control of the Magazine, he had a new vignette of the Palm House cut, based upon a drawing by its architect, Decimus Burton. Hooker, at his request, prepared an advertisement giving prominence to the importance of its association with the Royal Botanic Gardens at Kew. The advertisement promised to maintain its punctual appearance on the first day of every month, an unbroken record since its establishment nearly 60 years earlier. It would continue to observe its founder's objective of 'presenting to its readers the plants already cultivated in their gardens, as well as those among the recent importations that best deserve to be so'. The first issue under the new management came out in July 1845. The price per issue was still 3s.6d., but the cost of an uncoloured copy was reduced from 3s. to 2s.6d. One radical change was the relinquishment of line-engraving for lithography.

There were still 107 copper-plate engravers operating in London in 1840, but line engraving was waging a losing battle against economically more attractive processes such as wood-engraving and lithography. When Senefelder invented lithography which literally means stone writing, it represented a fundamental departure from the basic principles of graphic reproduction which had lasted for some 300 years. Lithography is based on the chemical antipathy of grease and water applied to a porous stone. Senefelder's discovery is essentially very simple. The artist draws with a greasy chalk on the surface of a stone, usually limestone ground smooth, which after dampening with water is covered with printer's ink. The ink, rejected by the water-saturated stone, is accepted by the greasy chalk drawing. The stone is then ready for printing. For the artist, the new process delivered him from the bondage of the engraver. In the confident hands of a botanical artist like W. H. Fitch, lithographs have an immediacy and spontaneity encountered usually only in original works of art. Francis Bauer was an instant convert. 'I certainly prefer the lithographs, as for coloured plates they are much better than line engraving',[2] he tells Sir William Hooker. In his *Strelitzia depicta* (1818), one of the earliest botanical works to adopt lithography, Bauer uses the process with an exquisite delicacy. Hooker tried to re-assure his conventional father-in-law of the improvements it offered, by some sample plates to demonstrate 'how very superior good lithographs are over line engravings'.[3] The first lithograph in the *Botanical Magazine* was *Fuchsia austromontana* (plate 4174)[4] and the first plate to carry the now familiar 'Fitch del et lith' was *Koellikeria argyrostigma* (plate 4175). Reeve produced the lithographic plates on his firm's press which he sold in 1854 to Vincent Brooks who then became the Magazine's lithographic printer.[5]

With his customary tact and diplomacy Sir William Hooker dedicated the first volume of the Third Series to the Earl of Lincoln, Chief Commissioner of

[2] May 3, 1837.

[3] Royal Botanic Gardens, Kew. Library (Archives). Sir William Hooker letters 1845–1851, item 76, July 9, 1845.

[4] In 1837 plates 31 and 32 in the *Companion to the Botanical Magazine* were lithographed but the regular use of this process was not until 1845.

[5] From plate 4782.

PLATE 17
Rhododendron hodgsonii. W. H. Fitch. Watercolour. (*Curtis's Botanical Magazine*, vol.
92, 1866, plate 5552). Discovered by W. Griffith in Bhutan in 1838, it was
collected in Nepal and Sikkim by Joseph Hooker who declared it to be 'one of
the noblest of the grand series of Rhododendrons that adorn the
Eastern Himalayan Mountains'.

New vignette of Palm House at Kew.
(On wrapper of *Curtis's Botanical Magazine*, July, 1845).

Woods and Forests, the department responsible for Kew Gardens. Sir William repeated this prudent gesture in dedicating the volume for 1848 to Lord Lincoln's successor, the Earl of Carlisle, with whom he enjoyed a friendly and sympathetic relationship.

Once in a while a new flower captures the imagination of the nation. Such was the case with the giant water lily discovered by Sir Robert Schomburgk in British Guiana in 1837. Schomburgk was overwhelmed by its 'gigantic leaves, five to six feet across, flat, with a broad rim, light green above, and vivid crimson below, floating upon the water. Quite in character with the wonderful foliage, were the luxuriant flowers, each consisting of many hundred petals, passing in alternate tints, from white to rose and pink'.[6] Four Europeans had already seen this 'vegetable wonder' but Schomburgk was determined to be the first to get living specimens safely back to England. Despite very careful packing, the plant was dead when it reached the Royal Geographical Society in London. But with the drawings made by Schomburgk's draughtsman, John Morrison, John Lindley recognized 'not only a new genus, but a plant of the most extraordinary beauty; fragrant, and of dimensions previously unheard of in the whole vegetable kingdom, except in the colossal family of Palms'. Thomas Bridges sent seeds of the water lily in bottles of moist earth from Bolivia in 1846, but the seedlings did not survive at Kew. Using herbarium specimens and Schomburgk's drawings, Sir William devoted the entire January 1847 issue of the *Botanical Magazine* to the *Victoria regia*[7] as it was named by John Lindley.

[6] *Magazine of Zoology and Botany*, vol. 22, 1838, p. 440.
[7] Now *Victoria amazonica*.

[88]

Fitch's emphatic and impulsive line brilliantly captures the monumentality of this spectacular aquatic plant in the four plates (4275–78) that elucidated 16 pages of text. Further consignments of seeds arrived in phials of water and by mid-summer Kew had nurtured many seedlings, one of which was presented to Joseph Paxton at Chatsworth. Paxton planted it in a heated tank in a glasshouse, cossetted it, and in November 1849 it flowered. Queen Victoria graciously received the first flower, the *Illustrated London News* published a sketch of Paxton's small daughter, Annie, standing diffidently on one of its broad leaves, and *Punch* applauded the event with a verse:

> 'On unbent leaf in fairy guise,
> Reflected in the water.
> Beloved, admired by hearts and eyes,
> Stands Annie, Paxton's daughter'.

Kew, the propagator of the seedlings, did not succeed in getting it to flower until 1850. The impact of this plant went far beyond the horticultural world; designers used it as a motif to decorate marble mantelpieces, its shape was adapted for light fittings and there was even a papier mâché *Victoria regia* cradle.

   The future of the *Botanical Magazine* seemed much more secure than that of its rival, the *Botanical Register*. It had been hoped that the merger with Robert Sweet's *British Flower Garden* in 1839 would 'render the *Botanical Register* the cheapest, as it is the most beautiful, of all the botanical periodicals, and eventually constitute it the completest and most authentic illustrated catalogue of plants in the world'.[8] Much cheaper horticultural magazines, however, were

[8] *Gentleman's Magazine*, vol. 14, 1838, p. 57.

Victoria amazonica (plate 4276). Drawn and lithographed by W. H. Fitch.

PLATE 18
Cattleya dowiana. W. H. Fitch. Watercolour. (*Curtis's Botanical Magazine*, vol. 93,
1867, plate 5618). This flamboyant orchid from Costa Rica flowered for the first
time in England in Veitch's Chelsea nursery in 1865.

just around the corner and when they arrived their presence was fatal for luxury magazines like the *Register*. Its publisher, Ridgway, offered to sell it to Reeve and, being declined, then proposed transferring his rights to the Horticultural Society of London subject to his still publishing it. The Horticultural Society was not interested in the proposition but, wishing to help, their Vice-President, J. C. Gowen, wrote to Hooker. 'Now I, and, of course, among other people interested in Horticulture will be inclined to substitute the *Bot. Mag.* and for this reason perhaps you will allow me to suggest the advisableness of placing that publication in a condition to become a harmonious continuation of the *Reg.* An annual supplementary title-page, or a new one, such as *The Bot. Mag & Register* could be added,' he hopefully suggested.[9] This proposed alliance between two former rivals came too late and the end of 1847 was also the end of the *Botanical Register*.

While these negotiations were proceeding, Sir William had his first disagreement with Reeve by requesting that his contractual payment of 13s. a plate be raised to a pound on the anticipated cessation of the *Botanical Register*. He needed the additional income to cover the increase in Fitch's salary from £125 to £150 in order to retain his services. Reeve reluctantly agreed but reminded Sir William that sales had hardly increased and that any profit was due to better management and to revenue from advertisements. By August 1848 sales had fallen by 50 copies to about 300 a month and Reeve announced certain economies to be imposed in 1849. Plates would be reduced to six in each issue and the folded plate which many subscribers disliked would be abolished. Hooker's revised remuneration as editor would be £2 for drawing and letterpress per plate and a pound for lithography. Hooker was also strongly urged to follow the example of other periodicals by including extensive cultivation notes. Sir William had no choice but to accept. The supplementary pages of the *Companion to the Botanical Magazine* ceased with volume 74 (1848) and from volume 75 John Smith, Curator at Kew, wrote practical horticultural advice under his own initials.

These economic measures and changes in presentation proved ineffectual remedies. A sampling of nineteenth-century British horticultural periodicals shows a dramatic rise in their number during the 1830s and 1840s. At least 15 new periodicals were founded in the 1830s but during the same period about 12 ceased publication. The vigorous competition engendered by this increased population of periodicals made the life of not a few of them insecure and brief.

Plagiarism was one means of lowering overheads for some editors. In 1850 Reeve had to caution W. S. Orr and Company, the publishers of the *Gardeners' Magazine of Botany*. 'The figures and descriptions of new plants in "The Gardeners' Magazine of Botany" copied from the "Botanical Magazine" have so prominent an appearance in the work that we must request you to discontinue the publication of them'.[10] The Belgian periodical, *Flores des Serres et des Jardins de l'Europe*, freely copied plates in the *Botanical Magazine*, the *Botanical Register*, J. D.

[9] Royal Botanic Gardens, Kew. Library (Archives). Lovell Reeve letters, p. 3, no date.
[10] *Ibid*, p. 96, February 3, 1850.

Cuphea cordata. Left: *Curtis's Botanical Magazine*, in 1846, (plate 4208).
Right: Copied with some adjustments in *Flore des Serres et des Jardins de L'Europe*,
vol. 2, 1846 (plate 7).

Hooker's *Rhododendrons of the Sikkim Himalaya* and other English works. In exasperation, Lovell Reeve eventually complained to the proprietor, Louis van Houtte, but at the same time made a proposal. 'We received your letter of the 4th inst. proposing to supply us gratis with plates for the Botanical Magazine in consideration of our furnishing you with the original drawings. Having fully considered the matter we beg to say we have no confidence in the undertaking and beg to decline. We have for some time past noticed the atrocious piracies that you continue to make on our property in the work and we are determined now to put a stop to it. Not only do you copy the plates in exact detail but you publish them in a dishonest manner falsifying the date. We observe that our beautiful and valuable plate of the Musa Ensete published for the first time in the Botanical Magazine of Jany 1 1861 appears in facsimile in your Flore des Serres dated 1859! Can anything be more dishonest? What can be the object of it except to make the public believe that *yours* is the *original* figure and *ours* a copy! Before taking any hostile measures to put a stop to this abominable system we have decided to make you the following offer. We will undertake to supply you with a coloured pattern of each plate before publication in consideration of your paying us 25 francs for each pattern. We will not agree to any selection'.[11] It is not known whether this proposal was implemented.

In 1852 Reeve reminded Hooker that when he bought the *Botanical Magazine* from Samuel Curtis 425 copies were coloured; that figure had now declined to 375 and in January sales were only 313. 'Under these circumstances I am *compelled* to submit a proposition to you for a reduction of terms – namely to pay £15 a month for what we now pay £18'. (In 1856 payment to Hooker for illustrating and describing the plants in each issue fell to £10.) If Hooker was unwilling to accept this revision of his salary, Reeve would 'make a total change in the contents and management of the Botanical Magazine agreeably with the spirit of the times'.[12] Reeve always wanted the Magazine to be more popular. Dispensing with John Smith's horticultural notes (surely a popular feature?) was one small economy enforced in 1852. The partial colouring of the plates – just the inflorescence and a leaf – was another money-saving device.

While Reeve was deep in this financial crisis, Samuel Curtis wrote from Jersey blandly claiming a family interest in the *Botanical Magazine*. Reeve was in no mood to bandy words or even to be civil. He peremptorily dismissed the claim. 'I am quite sure your family could not carry the work on without loss, and they would find it difficult to prove the copyright of any value. But be it valueless or not I shall most certainly contend on principle to my honest right to it. I am obliged to you for the offer of the back stock, but do not wish to encumber myself with it at any price. If your family attach any value to the name "*Curtis*" and wish to bring out a Botanical Magazine with this title they are perfectly welcome to use it!'.[13] Six years later Reeve declined an offer from Miss Curtis to buy her stock of uncoloured sheets and the copper plates on the grounds that there was little demand for the earlier volumes.

Anxious times though these years were for Reeve and Hooker, they were also the occasion when the pages of the *Botanical Magazine* were filled with exciting floral discoveries. In 1827 Nathaniel Wallich, Superintendent of the Royal Botanical Garden at Calcutta, collected seed of the magnificent *Amherstia nobilis* in a monastic garden in Burma. Its long racemes of vermilion flowers were daily offerings in the neighbouring Buddhist caves. The large lithographic plate of it in Wallich's *Plantae Asiaticae rariores* so impressed the Duke of Devonshire that one of his gardeners, John Gibson, was sent to India in 1835 with instructions to collect this as well as other plants. Two years later Gibson returned with a rich haul of orchids and two amherstias, one for the Duke and the other for the East India Company. The Duke's specimen had died on the homeward voyage, but the East India Company generously gave him the survivor. It was placed in the Painted Hall in Devonshire House in London where the Duke could admire it while he dined. Paxton tended it and though it flourished under his care it never flowered. That distinction fell to Mrs Louisa Lawrence at Ealing Park. Lord Hardinge, Governor General of India, had presented her with a young tree in 1847 and in

[11] Royal Botanic Gardens, Kew, Library (Archives). Lovell Reeve letters p. 382, September 9, 1862.

[12] *Ibid*, p. 152, February 26, 1852

[13] *Ibid*, p. 254, May 19, 1855.

Amherstia nobilis (plate 4453).
Drawn and lithographed
by W. H. Fitch.

1849, still only 3.3 m (11 ft) high, it became the first amherstia to flower in the British Isles. The first pendulous inflorescence was presented to Queen Victoria, the second to the editor of the *Botanical Magazine*. Within the confines of an octavo page only two open flowers, a bud, and a portion of a leaf conveyed something of the splendour of this tree to readers (plate 4453).

Size always impresses; whether it be the broad leaf of the *Victoria amazonica*, the height of the Wellingtonia or the bulk of *Echinocactus platyacanthus*. The *Echinocactus* had been the star exhibit of the Cactus house at Kew: 2.7 m (9 ft) high, 2.9 m (9.5 ft) in circumference and weighing just over a ton. An engraving of it was published in the *Illustrated London News* in 1846 and Sir William quite rightly thought it deserved a plate in the Magazine (plate 4559).

He also thought *Sequoiadendron giganteum* deserved two plates (4777–78). John Bidwell had come across a grove of these giant redwoods in California in 1841 but it was Veitch's collector, William Lobb, who brought back seed in 1853. Soaring to over 91 m (300 ft) and with a girth reaching 6 m (20 ft), they are the remnants of an ancient flora. 'The specimen felled at the junction of the Stanislav and San Antonio was above three thousand years old; that is to say, it must have been a little plant when Samson was slaying the Philistines, or Paris running away with Helen', so an excited John Lindley told readers of the

PLATE 19
Androsace pubescens. W. H. Fitch. Watercolour. (*Curtis's Botanical Magazine*, vol.
95, 1865, plate 5508). Joseph Hooker received this plant, a native of the
Pyrenees and the Swiss Alps, from Backhouse, the York nursery which
specialized in alpines.

Wellingtonia, now known as
Sequoiadendron giganteum (plate 4777).
Drawn and lithographed by
W. H. Fitch.

Christmas issue of the *Gardeners' Chronicle* in 1853. He named it *Wellingtonia gigantea* after the 'greatest of modern heroes', the Duke of Wellington. Indignant American botanists riposted by demanding it should be called *Washingtonia californica*. Quite indifferent to this nomenclatural dispute, Messrs Veitch soon had young plants for sale at their Exeter and Chelsea nurseries.

In 1860 the octogenarian Samuel Curtis died. Sir William, now in his mid-seventies, enlisted his son Joseph's aid in his latest clash with Lovell Reeve. For some time Reeve had been contemplating a new periodical to complement the Magazine, one specifically on florists' varieties of garden flowers. Despite reassurances, Sir William was understandably apprehensive about the effect it would have on the Magazine. He even thought of resigning as editor and starting another periodical himself. Reeve was extremely annoyed by this threat and the correspondence between himself and Joseph Hooker, always a plain-spoken man, became quite acrimonious. 'The Botanical Magazine is quite another matter. In this I have a copyright to protect', wrote Reeve. 'I do not expect your father to be bound to me for my profit to his own loss . . . . I cannot for one moment dispute your father's right to get a new Magazine published elsewhere, but when you add that you cannot see on what principle of honour I should seek to prevent him, you must excuse me telling you that under the present circumstances it would be far from dishonorable. Without waiting for the interview which I solicited, your father determines upon starting an opposition Magazine. I shall most assuredly do what I can to prevent the success of a rival, no matter from whence it proceeds, to a publication in which I have invested property, and which it is sought to crush'.[14]

Reeve's new venture, the *Floral Magazine*, was announced for publication in May 1860. The *Botanical Magazine*, under Sir William Hooker, would continue 'to represent the scientific department of Garden Botany' whereas the *Floral Magazine* would be devoted 'chiefly to meritorious varieties of such introduced plants only as are of popular character, and likely to become established favourites in the Garden, Hothouse, or Conservatory'. Thomas Moore, Curator of the Chelsea Physic Garden, was editor and W. H. Fitch, artist. Fitch had just left Sir William's regular employ to become a freelance artist. After only 16 issues both Moore and Fitch were asked to resign. 'Having the Botanical Magazine we not only do not want botanical subjects, but we want floral subjects treated both by editor and artist more *florally* if I may be allowed the expression', explained Reeve to Moore.[15] They were replaced by the clergyman-florist, the Rev. H. H. D'Ombrain as editor and James Andrews as artist. Andrews was in turn succeeded by W. G. Smith, F. W. Burbidge and finally in 1877 by W. H. Fitch's nephew, J. N. Fitch. It ceased publication in 1881 and 14 years later the firm of Lovell Reeve was still trying to dispose of a stock of *Floral Magazine* loose plates, offering them at 6d. or 1s., 'for screens, scrap-books, studies in flower-painting etc'.

It was never ever a threat to the *Botanical Magazine* which pursued its traditional policy of reviewing new and interesting species. *Lilium auratum* (plate 5338) created a sensation when it was exhibited in July 1862. This golden-rayed lily was brought back from Japan by John Gould Veitch. John Lindley, always easily moved to lyrical outbursts, was ecstatic. 'If ever a flower merited the name of glorious, it is this, which stands far above all other lilies, whether we regard its size, its sweetness, or its exquisite arrangement of colour. Imagine, upon the end of a purple stem no thicker than a ramrod, and not above two feet high, a saucer-

---

[14] Royal Botanical Gardens, Kew, Library (Archives). Lovell Reeve, Loose letters, item 323, May 11, 1860.

[15] *Ibid*, p. 364, April 29, 1861.

Lilium auratum (plate 5338).
Drawn and lithographed
by W. H. Fitch.

shaped flower at least ten inches in diameter, composed of six spreading, somewhat crisp parts, rolled back at their points, and having an ivory-white skin, thinly strewn with purple points or studs, and oval or roundish, prominent purple stains. To this add in the middle of each of the six parts a broad stripe of light satiny yellow, losing itself gradually in the ivory skin. Place the flower in a situation where side-light is cut off, and no direct light can reach it except from above, when the stripes acquire the appearance of gentle streamlets of Australian gold, and the reader who has not seen it may form some feeble notion of what it is'.[16]

If *Lilium auratum* rocked the horticultural world, the discovery of *Welwitschia mirabilis* reverberated around the botanical one. The first intimation that Europe had of this unusual cone-bearing plant was in a letter in 1860 to Sir William Hooker from Frederick Welwitsch, who was engaged in a scientific exploration of Portuguese territories in West Africa. Joseph Hooker made a careful analysis of specimens sent by Welwitsch, supplemented by drawings by Thomas Baines, and reported his conclusions at two meetings of the Linnean Society in 1862. The plant which was reputed to live for about 100 years has two enormous leaves, very leathery in texture, which, when fully grown, reach almost 2 m (6 ft) in length. Its discovery, Joseph Hooker considered 'the most wonderful, in a botanical point of view, that has been brought to light during the present century'.[17] He named this new genus of Gnetaceae, *Welwitschia*, after its discoverer. Fitch lithographed 11 plates of it for the *Transactions of the Linnean Society* and two for the *Botanical Magazine* (plates 5368–69).

Sir William impressed his readers with marvels like the *Welwitschia* and entertained them with botanical gossip. They learnt, for instance, that cannibals of the Fijian Islands used the leaves of *Solanum uporo* (plate 5424) to assist the digestion of human flesh. He quoted extensively from the African explorer,

[16] *Gardeners' Chronicle*, July 1862, p. 644.
[17] *Transactions of the Linnean Society*, vol. 24, 1864, p. 3.

Welwitschia mirabilis (plate 5368). Drawn and lithographed by W. H. Fitch.

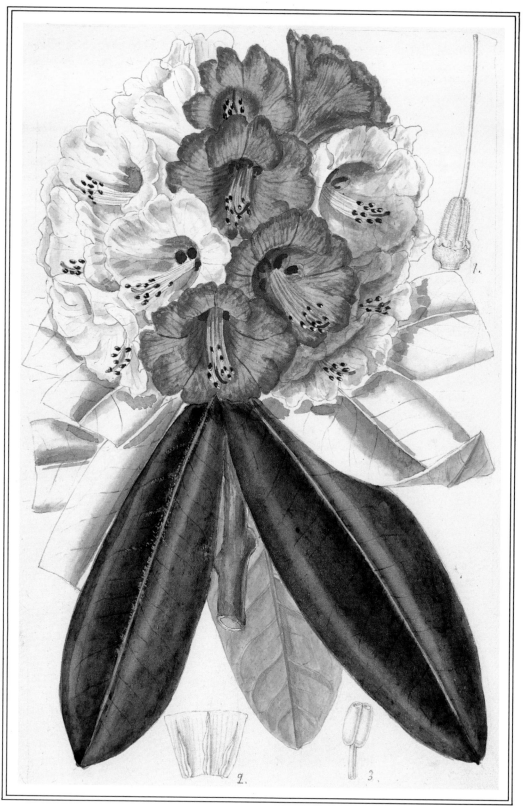

PLATE 20

Rhododendron niveum. Matilda Smith. Watercolour. (*Curtis's Botanical Magazine*, vol. 111, 1885, plate 6827). Raised at Kew from seed sent by Joseph Hooker from Sikkim in 1848–49.

James Bruce, on the culinary virtues of the banana-like *Ensete ventricosum*, 'When you make use of the *Ensete* for eating, you cut it immediately above the roots, and perhaps a foot or two higher if the plant is advanced in age; you strip the green from the upper part till it becomes white, where it is soft, like a turnip well boiled; if eaten with milk and butter, it is the best of all foods' (plates 5223–24). Sir William held a comprehensive view of plants: their identification and classification, their role in food, medicine and superstition and their enhancement of gardens. His *Companion to the Botanical Magazine*, unfortunately brought to a close in 1848 at Reeve's insistence, displays his catholicity of interest: botanical gardens in Russia and Portugal; botanical exploration in America, West Indies, Ceylon and Borneo; manufacture of paper; native cloths of the Pacific; and, of course, always the latest news on developments at Kew.

When Sir William became Director of the Royal Botanic Gardens at Kew, his dependence on other botanical gardens for plants to illustrate in the *Botanical Magazine* diminished; the combined contributions of Belfast, Dublin, Edinburgh and the Horticultural Society of London (which became the Royal Horticultural Society in 1861) for 1845 to 1864 amounted to only eight plants. The major nurseries became more accessible to him when he moved south. Hugh Low at Clapton, Jackson the orchid specialist at Kingston, Standish and Noble at Bagshot, Veitch at Chelsea and Exeter, and Lucombe and Pince, also at Exeter, readily sent him choice blooms. Surprisingly little came from private gardens. His near neighbours, the Duke of Northumberland at Syon House and Mrs Louise Lawrence in Ealing, between them, provided seven plants; there was a modest gathering from W. W. Saunders at Hillfield in Reigate, and three rhododendrons from Thomas Nuttall at Rainhill near Preston, collected by his nephew, Thomas Booth.

The plants described by Sir William during Lovell Reeve's proprietorship, reflect not only the fruits of botanical exploration but also his own personal interests. His promise to include ferns 'which are now such general favourites with cultivators' (plate 4698), is not unexpected from an eminent pteridologist; four appear in the early issues of 1854. The Palm House at Kew, possibly Sir William's greatest surviving memorial, brought palms to a greater prominence in the Magazine. 'The importance of the noble Palm-house at Kew, is now beginning to be felt by the blossoming of many rare Palms, which have never before produced flowers in any European collections' (plate 5139). In 1859 the Brazilian palm, *Syagrus romanzoffiana* (plate 5180), towering 18 m (60 ft) in the Palm House, flowered for the first time not only at Kew but probably also in the whole of Europe.

The floristic dominance of North America was being challenged by the discoveries farther south. Most of the species of that Victorian favourite, the fuchsia, came from Central and South America. Until the 1820s only two were in general cultivation in Britain in the conservatory and greenhouse: *Fuchsia coccinea* (plate 5740) and *F. lycioides* (plate 1024). *F. fulgens* (plate 3801), collected in Mexico by Hartweg for the Horticultural Society of London, became the parent of a vast progeny of hybrids. During the 1850s Kew Gardens was noted for its large and varied collection.

Ensete ventricosum (plate 5223).
Drawn and lithographed
by W. H. Fitch.

Australasia was represented in the Magazine by about 100 plants, only a dozen of which came from New Zealand. Acacias were popular because their seed remained viable during the long sea voyage, they were easy to grow, and their showy flowers made them eminently suitable for the greenhouse and large conservatory.

Fewer than 50 plates depicted South African plants. Most of the 24 from Sierre Leone had been collected by Thomas Whitfield on behalf of Lord Derby. Gustav Mann, a Kew gardener, succeeded Charles Barter in 1859 as botanist to the Niger Expedition. In 1861 his plants began to appear in the *Botanical Magazine* which, in 1887, acknowledged him as 'the most successful of all botanical explorers of Western tropical Africa; and who in the years 1860–80 contributed a prodigious number of seeds and living plants to Kew, as this Magazine testifies' (plate 6943).

Nearly half of the 25 plants from China illustrated during 1845 to 1864 owed their introduction to Robert Fortune, one of the Horticultural Society's greatest collectors. He had an unerring instinct for what would look well in an English garden. Such a plant was *Rosa* × *odorata* cv. 'Fortune's Double Yellow' (plate 4679) which caught his attention in a mandarin's garden, its 'masses of glowing yellowish and salmon-coloured flowers' completely covering an old wall. *Dicentra spectabilis* (plate 4458), lost to gardens soon after its first introduction in 1810, was reintroduced in 1846 by Fortune who found it on the artificial rocks of a grotto garden on the island of Chusan. The *flore pleno* variety of the popular *Camellia reticulata* shot up to a height of almost 4 m (13 ft) in the conservatory of W. B. Martin at Kingston in Surrey. 'At the beginning of October 1848, the multitude of flower-buds was so great that it was requisite for the health of the plant that 2,600 should be removed; and assuredly, though it was difficult to count them, nearly an equal amount (say 2,000 and we are sure we speak within bounds) were allowed to remain; and these were in the perfection of blossom in April of 1849' (plate 4976).

The *Botanical Magazine* chronicled the opening up of India and the East Indies. The collectors most frequently mentioned on the 167 plates of the Indian flora are Sir William's son, Joseph, Nathaniel Wallich of the Botanical Garden at Calcutta and Thomas Booth. George Gardner, now Superintendent of the Botanical Garden at Peradeniya and his successor, George Thwaites, sent plants from Ceylon. Orchids were collected by the Rev. Charles Parish in Burma and by Thomas Lobb in Java. Hugh Low collected in Borneo for Mackie's Clapton nursery.

When Sir William Hooker died in August 1865 he had edited 37 volumes of the *Botanical Magazine*, had written over 2,800 descriptions, and drawn many of the plates. Three months later Lovell Reeve died. Both men were energetic, strong-willed and ambitious, qualities guaranteed to strain any relationship. The decline in the circulation figures of the Magazine was perhaps outside their control; the advent of cheaper horticultural journals made it exceedingly difficult for quality periodicals to compete. Only Lovell Reeve's determination and Sir William Hooker's dedication could have ensured the survival of the *Botanical Magazine*. Shortly after his death, one of Reeve's authors paid him this just tribute. 'Both as an author and as a publisher he has left science deeply his debtor. His labours in the former capacity are well known and recognized; those in the latter though not so ambitious were scarcely less useful. He strove to divest scientific books of unnecessary technicalities, and to introduce correct teaching into popular works, so as to make them the fit commencement of the pursuit of real science'.[18]

[18] S. O. Gray, *British sea-weeds*, 1867, pp. ix–x.

A revised vignette of Palm House at Kew (on wrapper of *Curtis's Botanical Magazine*, from vol. 87, 1861).

8874–5.

PLATE 21
Gentiana farreri. Lilian Snelling. Lithograph by Huth. (*Curtis's Botanical Magazine*,
vol. 147, 1938, plates 8874–75). A well-known rock garden plant, collected by
Reginald Farrer in South Western Gansu in China in 1914.

✺ 6 ✺

THE TRANSPORTATION
OF PLANTS

THE migration of plants through the agency of man is as old as recorded history. The Romans, the Saxons and the Normans introduced plants that have now become part of the British flora. Early settlers to New England took with them comfrey for healing cuts and wounds, tansy for its innumerable remedies and for flavouring Easter puddings, and ground ivy as an ingredient in herbal tea. Ships carried fruit trees, cereals, vegetables and some of the familiar flowers of the English countryside to the young colony at Botany Bay in Australia. Much farther back in time, an Egyptian temple at Thebes records the importation of incense trees from Somalia during the reign of Queen Hatshepsut. About 1100 BC Tiglath Pileser I brought trees 'from the lands which I conquered, trees which none of the Kings my forefathers had planted: these trees I took and planted them in the parks of my country, these trees I planted in the parks of Assyria'. Elephants carried choice trees, their roots protected in balls of earth, from the borders of Kublai Khan's empire to his gardens in China.

This exodus of plants suffered a high mortality rate but many hardy trees and shrubs survived the comparatively short North Atlantic crossing. The diarist, John Evelyn, requested that trees from New England, destined for him, should have their roots protected by moss without the coating of honey that some botanists advocated. John Woodward's *Brief instructions . . . for collecting, preserving and sending over natural things* (1696) recommended that seeds should be well dried and bulbs and tubers packed in moss, cotton or sand.

· To the breadfruit tree, *Artocarpus communis*, we owe one of the most celebrated incidents in British nautical history. Captain William Dampier was the first European to describe it. He reported that the natives of Guam in the Pacific used it as bread; after baking and removing the outer crust, 'the inside is soft, tender, and white, like the crumb of a penny loaf'. Carl Solander, Joseph Banks's naturalist on Captain James Cook's first circumnavigation in 1768–71, called it 'the most useful vegetable in the world' and urged its cultivation. Planters in the West Indies, seeing it as a cheap source of food for their slave labour, petitioned George III for its transplantation there. John Ellis, a London merchant with business interests in the Caribbean, provided detailed instructions in his *Description of the Mangostan and Bread fruit* (1775) for the construction of boxes to carry these plants 'which would be extremely beneficial to the inhabitants of our West Indian Islands'. With the King's approval, H.M.S. *Bounty* was equipped to carry the breadfruit from the Pacific to the West Indies. William Bligh, the ship's captain, supervised its conversion into a floating container for plants. The

Left: Breadfruit or *Artocarpus communis*
(plate 2871). Rev. L. Guilding.
Engraved by J. Swan.

Below: Storage space on
H.M.S. *Bounty* for breadfruit trees.
(W. Bligh, *A voyage to the
South Sea*, 1792).

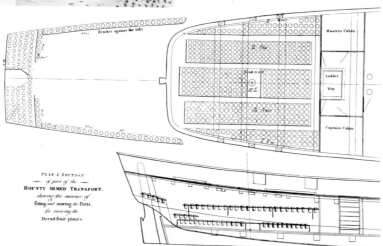

great cabin and much of the space between decks was adapted for the storage of
young trees. David Nelson, who had collected plants on Cook's third and last
voyage, joined the crew as gardener. His duties were precisely defined by Sir
Joseph Banks: he was to tend the trees, remove salt spray from the leaves with
fresh water and protect them from the ravages of rats and cockroaches. 'One day
or even one hour's negligence may at any period be the means of destroying all
the trees and plants which may have been collected, and from such a cause the
whole of the undertaking will prove not only useless to the public, but also to

yourself', was Banks's stern admonition.[1] Nelson was given an assistant, William Brown, to support him in the constant vigilance expected of him. Over 1,000 breadfruit from Tahiti were planted in tubs and the ship, fully laden, sailed for the West Indies. At the time of the well-documented mutiny, Captain Bligh recalled that 'the plants [were] in a most flourishing and fine order . . . . I even rejected carrying stock for my own use, and throwing away the hencoops and every convenience, I roofed a place over the quarter-deck and filled it with plants, which I looked at with delight every day of my life'.[2] Nelson remained loyal to Bligh, joined other members of the crew in an open boat, and died during its hazardous voyage. Brown stayed with the mutineers who unceremoniously threw the breadfruit overboard and sailed for Pitcairn Island.

When Bligh against all odds, eventually reached England, another ship was commissioned, H.M.S. *Providence*, which sailed for the Pacific under his command in 1791 in a further attempt to get the breadfruit to the West Indies. This time it was a successful mission, breadfruit and other plants were delivered to the botanical garden in St Vincent and in Jamaica, and plants collected in the West Indies were brought to the royal garden at Kew. They included *Epidendrum difforme* (plate 2030), *Peperomia clusiifolia* (plate 2943) and *Hillia tetrandra* (plate 7355). Sir William Hooker commemorated this story of courage, failure and ultimate success with three plates in the *Botanical Magazine* (plates 2869–71).

While H.M.S. *Providence* was in the Pacific, James Main was on board one of the East Indiamen, managed by James Slater, bound for China to bring back

[1] British Museum (Natural History). Botany Library. Dawson Turner transcripts of Sir Joseph Banks's correspondence, vol. 5, pp. 217–25.
[2] *Historical records of New South Wales*, vol. 1 (part 2), 1892, pp. 267–68. Bligh to Banks, October 13, 1789.

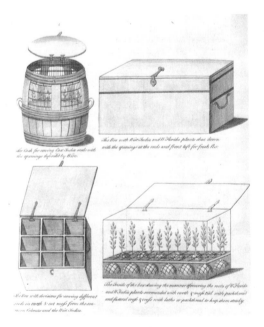

Containers recommended for transporting plants. (J. Ellis, *Directions for bringing over seeds and plants from the East Indies and other distant countries in a state of vegetation*, 1770).

PLATE 22

Gentiana sino-ornata. Lilian Snelling. Watercolour. (*Curtis's Botanical Magazine*, vol. 154, 1931, plate 9241). This popular gentian was discovered by George Forrest in 1904 at an altitude of 4,200–4,500 m (13,800–14,800 ft) in north-western Yunnan in China.

plants for Slater's garden in Leyton. Slater, frustrated by the high fatality among plants imported from China, had appointed Main to take care of them during the voyage. As an experiment, on behalf of the nurseryman, Conrad Loddiges, four sealed boxes of apple, pear, plum and rose trees were stowed in the hold and other boxes of soft fruits were placed on the deck and in the stern galley. By the time the ship reached Madras, all these plants, except the pear and apple, had died. On the return voyage from Canton, the poop deck and the stern were stacked with plants, packed in moss and protected from the salt spray by canvas curtains. Many had died when the ship reached the Cape, and others were lost after the rigging collapsed, crushing plant boxes on the deck. When the ship reached London in 1794, Slater was dead, and the few surviving plants were bought by George Hibbert at Clapham. The lesson James Main learnt from this experience was: *a)* the plants would have stood a better chance of survivial had he fewer to look after; *b)* had they been established in pots in Canton for a year or two before being shipped; *c)* had they left Canton in the Autumn when the Summer growth of the plants was over; and *d)* had they received the minimum of watering.

Sir Joseph Banks believed with an unshakeable faith that a plant cabin was the best means of guaranteeing the survival of plants on long voyages. Captains often refused to have these portable greenhouses, measuring anything up to 3.6 m (12 ft) by 1.8 m (6 ft) and weighing about 3 tons on their quarter-deck, fearing for their vessels' stability. One unhappy gardener with the custody of one on a ship bound for China complained to Sir Joseph Banks that 'the first mate does not approve of having a garden on the poop at all. He says it wracks the ship all to pieces. The captain agrees in the same story and when the beam creaks in the cuddy [i.e. the cabin] they all turn to me sometimes and damn the flower pots'. These cabins were used on the Australia and China routes with a success that relied largely upon the presence of a gardener or the attention of a vigilant crew. With some notable exceptions, ships' crews resented this additional responsibility and also the advice of John Lettsom, William Curtis's friend, that the captain should vacate part of the great cabin for the safe storage of these precious plants.

Some captains, however, took a personal pride in bringing back Chinese plants for the Horticultural Society of London. Captain Mayre of the *Atlas* in 1820 handed over a box of twelve varieties of chrysanthemums with the loss of just one plant. Captains Nesbitt, Wilson, Jamieson and Lindsay were equally attentive to the plants in their care. Credit for inculcating this devotion must be given to John Reeves, an inspector of tea at Canton from 1812 to 1831. But he always made sure that his plants were well-established in pots before entrusting them to co-operative crews. When he returned to England on the *Warren Hastings* in 1816, his personal attention saved 90 out of a consignment of 100 plants, an achievement which impressed John Livingstone, the East India Company's chief surgeon in China and a member of the Horticultural Society of London. In 1819 Livingstone proposed to the Secretary of the Society a number of measures to improve this trading in Chinese plants. Plants collected at the right time, potted in a suitable soil and with due attention to ventilation and

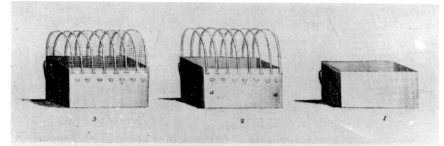

DIRECTIONS *for taking up* PLANTS *and* SHRUBS, *and Conveying Them by* SEA.

IN Order to take up the Plants advantageoufly, each Ship fhould be furnifhed with a Mattock and a Spade; with the Mattock a fmall Trench fhould be opened round the Plant intended to be taken up; the Spade fhould then be put under the Root, which muft be lifted up with a very large Ball of Earth furrounding it; the Ball may afterward be pared carefully with a Knife, and reduced as fmall as can be done without wounding any of the larger Roots.

Of each Kind the youngeft Plants of Shrubs and Trees that can be found fhould be taken; none of them fhould be above a Foot high; as young Plants are found by Experience to bear removing much better than old ones.

The moft convenient kind of Boxes for the Conveyance of Plants in long Voyages are made about Four Feet long, Two broad, and Two deep; thefe, when half filled with Earth, can be conveniently carried by two Men holding the Rope Handles fixed to their Ends.

Thefe fhould be filled about half full of Mould, with a few rotten Sticks or Leaves at the Bottom, and the Plants intended to be fent, planted in it, as foon after the Ship's Arrival as poffible. When the Ship is about to fail, and they are fent on board, Hoops are to be nailed to the Sides of the Box in fuch a Manner, that, arching over it, they may cover the Higheft of the Plants; fmall Ropes are to be twifted between thefe in the Form of a Net to prevent the Dogs or Cats from getting at them, and fcratching them up, on Account of the frefh Mould.

For each Box fo hooped and netted, provide a Canvas Cover, which may when put on entirely protect it; and to prevent this Cover from being loft or miflaid, nail it to one Side, and fix Loops or Hooks to the other, by which it may occafionally be faftened down.

The Captain who takes Charge of them, muft be particularly informed that the chief Danger Plants are liable to in Sea Voyages is occafioned by the minute Particles of Salt Water with which the Air is charged, whenever the Waves have white frothy Curls upon them; thefe Particles fall upon the Plants, and, quickly evaporating, leave the Salt behind, which choaking up the Pores prevents Perfpiration, and effectually kills the Plant; he therefore fhould never let the Covers be off, except on Days when the Wind is not fufficiently high, to beat the Water up into what the Seamen call White Caps; he muft not keep them always fhut up during the Voyage: for if he does they will mould and perifh by the Stagnation of the Air under the Covers; and if at any Time, by Accident or Neceffity, they fhould have been expofed to the Wind, when the Waves have White Caps, he muft be defired to water them well with frefh Water, fprinkling all the Leaves with it, to wafh off the Salt Drops which cover them. In this Manner Plants may be brought from almoft any Diftance; many come from *China* every Year in a flourifhing State.

If it is convenient to the Captain to give up a fmall Part of the Great Cabbin to the Plants, this is certainly by far the beft Station for them, nor are they much in the Way; as the Place which fuits them beft is clofe to the Stern Windows: in this Cafe they need not be furnifhed with their Canvas Covers, and they may frequently have Air, by opening the Windows when the Weather is quite moderate.

Ripe Seeds of all Kinds fhould alfo be brought Home; and it will be proper to fow in the Boxes of Earth, between the growing Plants, as many Sorts as poffible, fome of which may fucceed in Cafe of Failure of the Plants.

And if very fmall Bits of broken Glafs are mixed with the Earth, or thrown plentifully over its Surface, in the Boxes, it may prevent Mice or Rats from burrowing in it, and deftroying the tender Roots of the Plants and growing Seeds.

Fig. 1. Reprefents the Form of the Box.
—— 2. The fame, with Hoops and Loops, *a---a* for fecuring the Canvas.
—— 3. The fame, netted.

John Fothergill distributed this brief list of instructions to all his plant collectors. The plant container is shown in progressive stages of assembly: with the hoops for fastening a canvas cover and with netting to keep out inquisitive cats and other creatures.

watering on board ship stood a good chance of surviving the sea voyage. He calculated that the very high mortality rate was costing upwards of £300 to get a plant in a viable state to England.

The Society did not implement his recommendation that it should station a qualified gardener in Macao to supervise the collection and shipment of plants, but it did send one of its gardeners, John Potts, on a round trip in the *General Kyd* in 1821. John Damper Parks who made a similar journey in 1823 packed his square wooden pots into a box with a glass roof – the kind favoured by one of the Society's officers, John Lindley. Parks believed that azaleas, always difficult plants – not one of 500 Reeves shipped reached England alive – fared better in the form of cuttings under bell-jars.

A paper on bringing plants from India presented by N. Wallich to the Society in 1831, confirmed the experience of other botanists and gardeners; he made the additional point that plant cases should be portable for the convenience of the crew and that the plants themselves, on being unloaded, should convalesce in a hot house or conservatory before being sent to their destination. By this time a code of practice for the shipment of plants had evolved: they should be healthy specimens, well-rooted in a suitable soil (clay was not recommended); they should be despatched in the right season; the plant boxes should be small enough to be easily handled during storms; and they were to be protected from salt spray and watered regularly. Plants usually succumbed to over-drying, rotting and heating. Bulbs and tubers presented no problems as long as they were dry and in a dormant state, packed in paper or canvas bags. Epiphytic orchids were also easy to handle. The *Botanical Magazine* reported that Loddiges had received an *Oncidium bifolium* 'from a gentleman, who informed them that he brought it from Monte-Video, and that being hung up in the cabin without earth, it continued to flower a great part of the voyage home' (plate 1491). Another plant which enjoyed this aerial treatment was *Hoodia gordonii*, reaching 'Kew in perfect condition, having been carefully suspended in a wooden box without earth' (plate 6228).

Suspending ripe seeds in a bag from a cabin ceiling was reckoned a reliable method for their preservation, but more esoteric ways were investigated and tried. John Ellis coated them with wax or resin; John Lettsom embeddened them in yellow bees-wax; Linnaeus preferred dry sand; Wallich sent seeds from Nepal in tins of brown sugar. The *Botanical Magazine* mentioned that seeds of *Saraca indica* 'had been sent (packed in mould) by the Rev. Dr Carey of Serampore [in Bengal]. So skilful had been the mode of treatment pursued, that it flowered in great perfection when only four feet high' (plate 3018). On his departure for China in 1843, Robert Fortune carried out an experiment on the transit of seeds for the Horticultural Society. 'One lot was put up in bottles and sealed; a second was packed in paper and put into a box lined with tin; and a third was merely put in paper, and thrown loosely into a canvas bag to be hung up in my cabin'.[3] On arrival at Hong Kong some of the seeds in the sealed bottles were mouldy, others were dry and had vegetated. Those in tin-lined boxes and canvas bags were still viable. Fortune preferred bags but regretfully admitted that 'it is often

³ *Journal of the Horticultural Society of London*, vol. 3, 1848, p. 41.

difficult to induce captains of ships or others to allow packages of this kind to be swinging about in cabins'.

Soon, however, a new system for the transportation of plants was to be devised and tried, a method that was to increase substantially the introduction of exotics and thereby change dramatically the composition of English gardens.

Nathaniel Bagshaw Ward was a London physician, and like so many of his profession, also a serious naturalist. In a letter to Sir William Hooker (which Sir William judged of sufficient importance to publish entire in the *Companion to the Botanical Magazine* in 1836), he reported the incidental results of an experiment he had carried out about 1830. About a month after he had buried a sphinx

Wardian case. (N. B. Ward, *On the growth of plants in closely glazed cases*, 1852, p. 71).

moth chrysalis in some moist mould in an enclosed glass bottle, he observed the appearance of a fern and a grass which continued to grow without any attention from him. Further experiments with flowering plants and ferns led to his discovery that provided glass bottles and cases were sealed and given adequate light to promote photosynthesis, the transpiration of the plants saturated the air within the glass case with water vapour which in turn condensed on the glass and moistened the soil in a continuing cycle. Under such conditions, plants could survive for a remarkably long time without further watering. With the current craze for ferns in mind, Ward marketed his discovery as 'Wardian Cases of Ferns or Ward's Portable Greenhouses'. Before long every fashionable drawing room had a Wardian case, designed with Gothic exuberance or an extravagence of rustic filigree, displaying tropical ferns and other suitable plants.

But Ward realized that there was a far more important use for his case, 'that of the conveyance of plants upon long voyages. Reflecting upon the causes of the failure attending such conveyance, arising chiefly from deficiency or redundancy of water, from the spray of the sea, or from the want of light in protecting them from the spray, it was, of course, evident that my new method offered a ready means of obviating all these difficulties'.[4] In 1833 two stoutly built Wardian cases were filled with ferns, grasses and some flowering plants which during the four-month voyage to Australia, lashed to the poop deck, were watered only once. They arrived at Sydney healthy and with a solitary primrose gloriously in flower. The Australian plants which refilled the two cases were never watered during the whole of the return voyage lasting eight months. George Loddiges who took delivery of them immediately adopted these cases for the importation of plants for his nursery. In 1834 the first Wardian case reached New York with its contents 'as fresh and healthy as when they left London'. Captain Gillies of the *Hibernia* told the *Gardener's Magazine* in 1836 how he had brought back a glazed box which 'was never opened during a voyage of five months. When we arrived in England, the plants were all in beautiful health, and had grown to the full height of the case, the leaves pressing against the glass'.

John Lindley recommended the use of Wardian cases to the Duke of Devonshire whose gardener at Chatsworth, John Gibson, was about to leave for India in 1835 to collect orchids and, hopefully, the much coveted *Amherstia nobilis*. Before he left Gibson visited Loddiges at Hackney for advice and related what he saw to Joseph Paxton, the head gardener at Chatsworth. 'The description of the case is that in the first place they are styled airtight boxes, the tops are screwed on and the plants never allowed to get any water or air after being well watered when first put in the case. As the water evaporates without escaping from the box and condenses it is said that it is found to be a sufficient supply during the voyage'.

Robert Fortune, 'supplied with fowling piece and pistols, and a Chinese vocabulary', was sent to the Far East by the Horticultural Society of London in 1843 to 'collect seeds and plants of an ornamental or useful kind'. He took with him three Wardian cases to assess 'the effect upon the plants of the various circumstances to which they may be exposed during the voyage'.[5] There was still some uncertainty about the reliability of these cases but Fortune's success with them completely vindicated their use. He returned to London in May 1846, after just over four months at sea, with 18 Wardian cases on the poop of the ship. 'The plants arrived in excellent order', he wrote, 'and were immediately conveyed to the garden of the Horticultural Society of London'.[6]

The *Botanical Magazine* quoted at length his difficulties during a later trip to China to introduce the Golden Larch, *Pseudolarix amabilis*. 'I used every means in my power to introduce its seeds in large quantities and good condition. They were sent by overland mail, some in letters and some in small packages, for several years in succession, and were often sown in England in less than two months from the time they were gathered from the tree in China. Out of all sent home only one despatch vegetated freely; all the others were complete failures. All the plants of any size now in England were dug up in the woods of China and

[4] *Companion to the Botanical Magazine*, vol. 1, 1836, p. 319.
[5] *Journal of the Royal Horticultural Society*, vol. 68, 1943, pp. 162–65.
[6] R. Fortune, *Three years' wanderings in the Northern Province of China*, 1847, p. 405.

Wardian case in use at Kew Gardens during the 1930s.

sent home in Wardian Cases' (plate 8176). He successfully used the cases to transport nearly 20,000 tea plants from Shanghai to the Himalayas for the East India Company.

There were, of course, failures with Wardian cases, especially during the early days of their use. Half the plants George Gardner despatched from Brazil in six large Wardian cases were dead on arrival but he attributed this mishap to badly constructed boxes. R. C. Gunn in Tasmania complained to Sir William Hooker about the number of dead and dying plants in the Wardian cases he received. Fortune maintained that such casualties could be eliminated if the following precautions were taken. 'Do not move them from the poop, never allow them to be opened; should any accident happen to the glass repair it immediately, either with glass, or, where that cannot be had, a piece of thin board will answer the purpose; in stormy weather, when there is any probability of spray coming over the poop, throw an old sail over the cases; and lastly, never allow the sailors to throw a drop of water over them when they are washing decks in the morning'.[7]

When such precautions were observed, plants usually reached their destination perfectly healthy. Loddiges told Sir William Hooker that 'whereas I used formerly to lose nineteen out of every twenty of the plants I imported during the

[7] *Journal of the Horticultural Society of London*, vol. 2, 1847, p. 119.

voyage, nineteen out of the twenty is now the average of those that survive'. Sir William who had made good use of the cases to forward plants from Kew to the colonies dedicated the 1852 volume of the *Botanical Magazine* to Ward 'whose invention of the closely glazed cases has contributed so much to the enriching of our gardens with plants from the most distant regions'.

The Wardian case with its glazed roof protected by wooden slats was used by Kew up to the Second World War. Notwithstanding its general acceptance, other methods of moving plants over great distances were tried. While Joseph Hooker was in Calcutta in 1850, an American ship bringing ice to India unloaded some boxes of frozen plants. The fruit trees were in the 'most perfect state'. Once they had thawed out and established themselves they were sent to the foothills of the Himalayas in Wardian cases. Ice was also used to preserve *Primula sonchifolia*, collected in Upper Burma in 1930. 'Through the good offices of . . . the Governor of Burma, the plants were transported through Burma in sections of bamboo stems with ice packing, transferred to the cold storage of a steamer and brought home safely as a gift to his Majesty George V' (plate 9527).

Short-lived seeds were put into vacuum flasks but the aeroplane was the obvious means of transporting both seeds and plants in the shortest possible time. The *Botanical Magazine* mentions that Lionel de Rothschild flew in cuttings of *Erica pillansii* (plate 9676) about 1934 from South Africa for his garden at Exbury. Frank Ludlow and George Sherriff were among the first collectors to make regular use of air transport.

William Curtis followed the practice of other gardeners by saving the earth from the pots in which plants had been transported from overseas in the hope that any stray seeds would germinate. Through scattering such soil he obtained *Wahlenbergia vinciflora* (plate 691). In a similar fortuitous manner Charles Greville acquired *Adina globiflora* (plate 2613) from China. The soil in various boxes of ferns yielded *Streptocarpus polyanthus* (plate 4850) and *S. wendlandii* (plate 7447) from South Africa and the grass *Crytochloa concinna* (plate 7469) from Costa Rica. Also, the Australian sundew, *Drosera spathulata* (plate 5240), was a bonus in the soil of a Wardian case.

Ranunculus asiaticus albus.
(Mr W. B. Turrill.)

Lilian Snelling.

PLATE 23
Ranunculus asiaticas var. *albus*. Lilian Snelling. Watercolour. (*Curtis's Botanical
Magazine*, vol. 157, 1934, plate 9380). Widely distributed throughout the eastern
Mediterranean; in Crete the flowers are commonly white or pale-coloured
whereas in Iran they are usually scarlet or orange.

7

GLASSHOUSES AND GARDENS

I N 1925 the *Botanical Magazine* commented on 'the changes in interest, taste and, what is perhaps more important, in horticultural skill which determine from time to time the composition of the flora of our gardens and glasshouses' (plate 9061). In Regency England stoves and conservatories glowed with the flora of the British colonies in South Africa and Australia and the pages of the Magazine celebrated their arrival. Ten species of the Australian flowering shrub, *Pultenaea*, were figured between 1800 and 1835. The South African protea claimed eight plates up to 1810 and another seven between 1810 and 1827 but only another four new species were illustrated right up to the 1920s. In the 1820s, 11 species of *Prostanthera* from Australia were in cultivation; about a century later only one of that number appears to have survived in British greenhouses. In 1811 the royal garden at Kew grew over 40 species of stapelias and 37 of epiphytic orchids. With the passage of barely 50 years the collection of stapelias had diminished drastically whereas the orchids had expanded to about 400 species. In those early days plant-houses or stoves were heated with hot air in which orchids soon perished but proteas and banksias flourished. The *Botanical Magazine* repeatedly made the point that the neglect of these plants from South Africa and Australia was due not only to a loss of horticultural expertise but also to 'the introduction of those improved systems of heating houses and that incessant watering, that favours soft-wooded tropical plants' (plate 6558).

The precursor of the Victorian glasshouse was the orangery, the winter home of citrus fruit and exotics which were displayed in tubs out of doors during the summer. Often designed by distinguished architects like Vanbrugh, Wren, Adam and Chambers, they dignified the landscape with their classical proportions. Even after their conversion to glasshouses by a substitution of glass for their tile or slate roofs, they were not really suitable for plants demanding plenty of light. As the garden designer Humphry Repton, observed at the time, 'the numerous tribe of geraniums, ericas, and other exotic plants, requiring more light, have caused a very material alteration in the construction of the greenhouse'. New large plant-houses like those at Alton Towers and Syon House were designed in a transitional style between the solidity of the orangery and the extravagant glazing of Victorian conservatories.

The construction of glasshouses was discussed with impressive technical virtuosity by members of the Horticultural Society of London. Thomas Knight in his presidential address in 1811 regretted that 'not a single building of this kind has yet been erected in which the greatest possible quantity of space has been obtained, and of light and heat admitted, proportionate to the capital expended'. In a letter to Sir Joseph Banks and subsequently published in 1816 in

A cool conservatory laid out in a 'natural style'.
(*The Garden*, vol. 1, 1872, p. 289).

the *Transactions* of the Society, Sir George Mackenzie was one of the first to advocate curvilinear glass roofs. J. C. Loudon who deplored 'lean-to shed-looking glass roofs' enthusiastically supported the concept of curvilinear roofs which combined functionalism with elegance. 'Instead of the usual conservatories attached to mansions, imagine a lofty arched roof wholly transparent, and joined to it according to the magnitude and style of the mansion, globular projections, elevated circular towers surmounted by Eastern domes of glass, or other beautiful or characteristic forms, all transparent and of permanent duration'.[1] Loudon's inventive genius added 'ridge and furrow' glazing and a heated wrought-iron bar to these revolutionary innovations in glasshouse design.

The latest developments in industrial technology reduced masonry to a minimum. Cast-iron beams were used for the first time in 1801 in the building of a cotton mill. In 1808 Repton designed a slender cast-iron pheasantry for the Royal Pavilion at Brighton. Six years later the conservatory Nash built for the Royal Lodge at Windsor was constructed of cast-iron trellised pillars and glass. W. and D. Bailey to whom Loudon had transferred his patent for his glazing bar built many elegant metal conservatories in the 1820s. The great curvilinear domed conservatory built for Mrs Beaumont at Bretton Hall in Yorkshire had wrought-iron sash bars. The principal nurseries in London were early converts to the curvilinear conservatory: Rollisson, Knight's Exotic Nursery and Loddiges which had the world's largest hot house for palms and also a camellia house with a glass roof 36.5 m (120 ft) long.

In 1818 the *Botanical Magazine* reported that 'the stoves, conservatories and greenhouses, belonging to Messrs Loddiges and Sons, are now entirely heated by steam, upon a principle that is simple and perfectly safe, and there is little doubt but that it will be ere long generally adopted, and that the use of steam will form a new era in the history of hothouses' (plate 2001). The conventional heating system of orangeries and conservatories until the end of the eighteenth century relied upon flues built into the thickness of walls and under floors with perhaps a tan-pit to provide additional heat. Potted plants would be stood in a fermenting mass of tan-bark which the *Botanical Magazine* condemned as 'a most troublesome and expensive article'. Neither method offered any means of efficient temperature control, and smoke and fumes escaping through cracked flues polluted the air. Steam, circulating through perforated pipes, had by the 1820s superseded these traditional methods but its popularity was brief. The hot-water boilers of the 1830s at last offered a reliable system of controlled heat.

As blown glass could not be made in large sheets, early nineteenth-century conservatories were glazed with panes 'ecclesiastically small'. Only after improvements in pouring and rolling processes in the 1830s did long lengths of sheet glass become available. In 1845 the prohibitive 'duty was taken off glass, and there was henceforth free trade in the sunshine and the glorious light of heaven'. A modest greenhouse was now within the reach of everyone and a privileged few could afford that exuberant expression of Victorian prosperity and confidence, the large conservatory – an insubstantial bubble of glass held

[1] J. C. Loudon, *Sketches of curvilinear hothouses*, 1818, p. 1.

together by a filigree of metal. The architecturally inspired orangery had evolved into an engineer's concept of functional simplicity.

The wealthy had houses built for particular plants. Ericas and succulents, it was agreed, needed a perfectly dry environment, pelargoniums the maximum of light, camellias, rhododendrons and magnolias would be good neighbours in a cool house, and orchids and exotic ferns thrived in humidity. Then there were vineries, pineries, peach houses, fig houses and aquatic houses. Lord Powis's seat at Walcot had 'a lofty hot house 400 feet long and between thirty and forty wide, constructed for the cultivation of the Mango and other rare tropical fruits' (plate 4510).

Joseph Paxton's large conservatory at Chatsworth was the realization of Loudon's dream of enclosed gardens with 'winding walks, fountains, and even plots of grass and ponds of water, so that the only difference between them and the real garden, is that glass intervenes between the summit of their trees and the sky'. Built between 1836 and 1841, it extended nearly 91 m (300 ft) and rose above 18 m (60 ft); within its acre of landscaped tropical vegetation there was a huddle of rockwork, crystals reflected in a pool and the celebrated *Amherstia nobilis* which stubbornly refused to flower. Wood was the main component of Paxton's creation but Decimus Burton and Richard Turner chose wrought-iron for the Palm House at Kew. Just a few years after its completion in 1848, Kew's Director, Sir William Hooker, was pleased to tell subscribers that 'the Palms in the noble house recently built for their reception in the Royal Gardens of Kew, are beginning to feel the benefit of their translation from the old stoves, many of them growing with a rapidity almost incredible to those who do not witness it, exhibiting something of their native character, and not a few of them bearing flowers and fruit; so that we shall take advantage of our success, and from time to time present figures in the pages of our Magazine' (plate 4773).

The flowers flourishing in all these glasshouses inevitably made an impact upon the Magazine which, from the late 1840s, includes many more hot-house plants. 'There never was a period, perhaps', wrote the editor of the *Botanical Magazine*, 'when so many splendid new plants were introduced to our stoves and greenhouses as at present' (plate 4355).

Regarded by mid-Victorians as being just as important as the music or billiard room, the conservatory was attached to the house, usually on its southern side. Subtropical plants, carefully chosen for their foliage, were planted in beds; fern-covered rocks bordered a meandering path; water splashed or trickled into a pool; clematis climbed slender pillars. The romantic novelist, Charlotte M. Yonge, saw it as 'a real bower for a maiden of romance, with its rich green fragrance in the midst of winter. It is like a picture in a dream. One could imagine it a fairy land, where no care, or grief, or weariness could come'. This green haven gradually became a favourite room for parties, and tables and chairs eventually relegated plants to tubs and shelves around the walls. The conservatory was a rarity by Edwardian times when gardeners deserted hot-house plants for the more hardy species from the Sino-Himalayas. The fashion was now for natural gardening, a style strenuously promoted by William Robinson who so abhorred glasshouses that he demolished all those at Gravetye

Mr Bessemer's conservatory at Denmark Hill, Camberwell.
(*The Garden*, vol. 1, 1872, p. 170).

when he purchased the property. Just as Paxton's conservatory at Chatsworth symbolized the beginning of an era of great glasshouses so did its demolition in 1920 signify its demise. Except in botanical gardens, they had become an expensive anachronism.

It is impossible to define a typical Victorian garden. It was often a pastiche of the picturesque and the geometrical, of exotic and indigenous trees, of standard roses rising above drifts of old-fashioned flowers or in regimented beds, of serpentine walks and shrubberies, of stretches of lawn with a Wellingtonia or a Monkey Puzzle tree standing guard, and with a rustic seat or arbour from which to contemplate it all. It was a time when old friends like the erica and oxalis were abandoned and new ones made: chrysanthemums, tuberous begonias, calceolarias, fuchsias, tea roses, lilies and orchids. The 1840s witnessed a frenetic activity in the gardening world. In 1805 only one horticultural society existed; by 1842 there were more than 200. The boom in horticultural journals had not yet abated; in 1841 the *Gardeners' Chronicle*, which is still with us, was launched. In the same year the old royal garden at Kew was elevated to a national botanic garden (the nineteenth century was the heyday of botanical gardens, both national and local). John Lindley gave gardening scientific respectability with his *Theory and practice of horticulture* (1840). J. B. Whiting's *Manual of flower gardening for ladies* (1849) earnestly commended gardening as 'a peculiarly fitting employment for a refined and gentle female'. Jane Loudon, infected by her husband's missionary zeal, pioneered gardening for women with a daunting determination. Birkenhead Park, begun in 1844, heralded the great Victorian park designed for recreation and fresh air. In 1840, William Lobb, the first of a distinguished line of Veitch collectors, sailed from Plymouth for South America. 'Our eminent and spirited nurserymen', as the *Botanical Magazine* appreciatively described them, dictated public taste through their catalogues and their collectors.

The Veitch dynasty was founded by John Veitch when he opened the Killerton Nurseries near Exeter in 1808; 24 years later he moved into Exeter itself. In 1853 the firm purchased the old-established nursery of Messrs Knight and Perry in the King's Road, Chelsea; eventually the Exeter and London establishments became independent but still controlled by members of the Veitch family. Earlier nurserymen had employed the occasional collector but it was the Veitches who used collectors on a large scale; between 1840 and 1906 they had twenty-two collectors working for them including three members of the family. William Lobb was sent to South America to collect, among other things, seeds of the Monkey Puzzle, *Araucaria araucana*. Conifers were a speciality of James Veitch and Son. Lobb collected several species of pine from California and the cones of the Wellingtonia. John Gould Veitch introduced a number of hardy conifers from Japan, the best-known being the Japanese larch, *Larix leptolepis*. William Lobb's brother, Thomas, spent 17 years in South and South East Asia collecting for the Veitches and hot-houses were filled with his haul of orchids, rhododendrons and nepenthes. The modern hybrid tuberous begonias and gigantic hippeastrums owe a great deal to the botanical explorations of Richard Pearce. John Gould Veitch just beat Robert Fortune in the introduc-

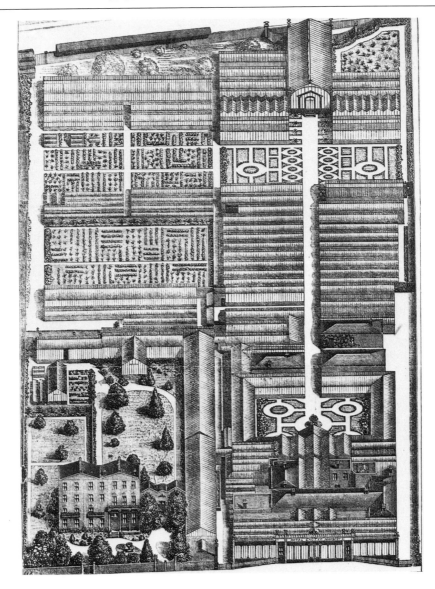

The original Veitch nursery at Chelsea.
(J. H. Veitch, *Hortus veitchii*, 1906, frontispiece).

tion of *Lilium auratum* by a few weeks; had he failed, however, his name would still
be remembered for the popular 'Virginia creeper,' *Parthenocissus tricuspidata*.
After several years in Japan, Charles Maries went to China where he found the
witch hazel, *Hamamelis mollis* (plate 7884), considered by some to be the finest
hardy plant ever to come out of that country. The Chinese flora was
scrupulously investigated by E. H. Wilson, the greatest of all the Veitch
collectors. By 1906 no fewer than 422 plates in the *Botanical Magazine*
acknowledge Veitch as their source,[2] and in 1910 the Magazine recorded its

[2] J. H. Veitch, *Hortus Veitchii*, 1906, pp. 21–26.

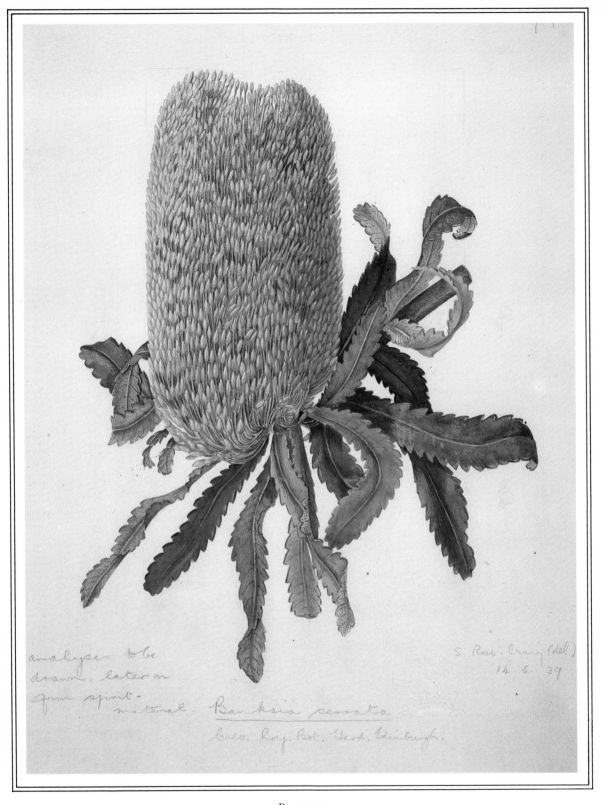

PLATE 24

Banksia serrata. Stella Ross-Craig. Watercolour. (*Curtis's Botanical Magazine*, vol.
163, 1942, plate 9642). This is a common shrub or tree on the coastal fringe of
Queensland to Victoria.

indebtedness by dedicating vol. 136 to Sir Harry J. Veitch, the great-grandson of the founder, and the last proprietor of the firm which closed in 1914.

Although cuttings of pelargonium and heliotrope were wintered in garden frames for planting out in beds, it needed the repeal of the glass tax and the availability of dwarf varieties to make wholesale bedding-out practicable. With cheaper glasshouses by the late 1840s, many middle-class families could afford to set one aside for raising suitable half-hardy annuals and tender perennials for bedding out. Initially, gardeners sought to catch the eye with a massing of bold colours – scarlet geraniums, yellow calceolarias, blue lobelias and purple verbenas – with such a lack of subtlety that, said William Robinson, compelled 'those with finer perceptions . . . to enquire for the Parsley bed, by way of relief'. Such highly-coloured stridency was anathema to Shirley Hibberd, a garden writer who never minced his words. 'The stereotyped repetition of scarlet geraniums and yellow calceolarias is in the last degree vulgar and tasteless and the common disposition of red, white and blue are better adapted to delight savages than represent the artistic status of a civilized people'. Inter-planting with foliage plants like coleus and variegated-leaved pelargonium achieved a greater degree of harmony and a more relaxed fusion of colour. It was not long before these colour-orchestrated beds migrated to ribbon borders in the lawn.

Carpet-bedding at Stoke Rochford near Grantham, Lincolnshire.
(*Gardeners' Chronicle*, 1879, p. 45).

Bedding-out was most effective and appropriate as a formal pattern on the broad terraces of large houses such as Trentham and Shrublands. It was once said, tongue in cheek, that the social standing of the gentry was assessed by the extent of their bedding-out list: 10,000 plants for a squire, 20,000 for a baronet, 30,000 for an earl and 50,000 for a duke. Carpet-bedding was a degenerate form of bedding-out – a pictorial mosaic of dwarf plants. It still survives in the floral clocks and coats of arms of municipal parks and sea-side promenades.

By 1867 the *Botanical Magazine* had figured 23 species of *Calceolaria* and doubtless disapproved of their integration in bedding-out schemes. Sir Joseph Hooker never concealed his dislike of 'the rage for "bedding-out plants" which now monopolize the once varied borders of English gardens . . . . It is hoped that the time will yet come when the taste for really beautiful and interesting plants will reign again, and replace the present passion for a blaze of gaudy colours along our garden walks' (plate 5621).

It was during the late 1840s that the first of Sir Joseph Hooker's gleanings from the Sikkim Himalaya reached Kew, among them new species of rhododendrons whose invasion of gardens assisted the easing of that precise formality encouraged by bedding out. *Rhododendron*, one of the largest of all genera of trees and shrubs, has a very wide geographical distribution, the greatest concentration being on the slopes and in the valleys of the Sino-Himalayan chain of mountains. John Parkinson's *Paradisi in sole paradisus terrestris* (1629) was one of the first manuals to recommend rhododendrons for the garden – in this instance, *R. hirsutum*. The first thousand plates in the *Botanical Magazine* figure only six rhododendrons which include *R. ponticum* (plate 650) and *R. maximum* (plate 951). *R. ponticum*, one of the few European species of the genus, was, according to the *Botanical Magazine*, sold in the London markets 'to ornament our houses in the Spring'. *R. maximum*, collected by John Bartram in North America, flowered for the first time in England in 1756 at the Mile End nursery of James Gordon. It was still a comparative rarity in 1775 when it was one of the dearest shrubs for sale in the nursery catalogue of Telfords of York. *R. caucasicum* (plate 1145) from Mount Caucasus and *R. catawbiense* (plate 1671) from the Catawba River in North America became the principal parents of many well-known hardy hybrids. These few species adapted so readily to the climate and soil of the British Isles that at Bagshot Park in 1829 they had to be ruthlessly thinned out. In 1842 Sir William Hooker complimented the Countess of Rosslyn who had 'taken great pains to form at Dysart House, an unusually extensive collection of the different species and superb varieties of *Rhododendron* . . .; they thrive and flower in a manner certainly not surpassed in any collection in Britain' (plate 3947). Messrs Veitch sent Sir William *R. javanicum* in 1847, found by their collector Thomas Lobb in Java, with the enthusiastic comment that it was 'certainly one of the finest things ever introduced to our gardens' (plate 4336). When in November of the same year Joseph Hooker sailed for India, rhododendrons must have been high on his list of plants to seek and collect.

The first Indian rhododendron – *R. arboreum* – had been collected by Captain Hardwicke; James Sowerby drew it for J. E. Smith's *Exotic Botany* (1804) and the

Left: *Rhododendron javanicum* (plate 4336). Drawn and lithographed by
W. H. Fitch. Collected by Thomas Lobb in Java for Messrs Veitch.
Right: *Rhododendron ciliatum* (plate 4648). Drawn and lithographed by W. H. Fitch.
It flowered at Kew in 1852 while only 18cm (7in) high.

white variety appeared in the *Botanical Magazine* in 1834. Wallich sent seeds of
R. arboreum and another Himalayan species, *R. campanulatum* (plate 3759) which
Joseph Hooker reintroduced some 25 years later.

The unexplored kingdom of Sikkim had been suggested as a promising place
for new plants and it was there that Hooker found many of his rhododendrons.
Exhilarated but exhausted he wrote to his father: 'If your shins were as bruised as
mine tearing the interminable Rhododendron scrub up to 10–13,000 feet, you
would be as sick of the sight of these glories as I am'. Their seeds were harvested
and sent to Sir William and the first of them to flower at Kew was *R. ciliatum*
(plate 4648) in 1852. Sir William persuaded Lovell Reeve to publish an
illustrated account of some of these flamboyant flowers. The first ten plates of
Rhododendrons of Sikkim–Himalaya appeared in 1849. W. H. Fitch's incisive line
superbly recreated these exotic blooms from Joseph's dried specimens and
meagre field sketches. Its speedy publication was applauded by *The Athenaeum*.
'That he should have ascended the Himalaya, discovered a number of plants,
and that they should be published in an almost unequalled style of magnificent
illustration, in less than eighteen months – is one of the marvels of our time'.

Of the 25 rhododendrons published by the *Botanical Magazine* between 1852
and 1866, 14 were credited to Joseph Hooker. As each new rhododendron
bloomed it excited the mounting admiration of his father. Sir William praised
'the great size and beauty of the fragrant flowers' of *R. dalhousiae* (plate 4718)

Alstroemeria violacea. Stella Ross-Craig. Watercolour. (*Curtis's Botanical Magazine,*
vol. 165, 1948, N.S. plate 42). Although this Chilean plant was discovered
during the mid-nineteenth century, it was not introduced into
cultivation until 1939.

which first flowered at Dysart House. After *R. dalhousiae* he hailed *R. maddenii* 'the noblest of the Sikkim Rhododendrons' (plate 4805). *R. grande* (plate 5054) was ranked 'among the finest of the many fine Rhododendron discoveries of Dr Hooker'; its rival, *R. griffithianum* (plate 5065) was 'in some respects the finest of the genus'. But in this delirium of delight perhaps the accolade belongs to *R. fulgens* of which the *Botanical Magazine* emphatically declared 'none can vie in colour with the subject of the present plate' (5317). Joseph Hooker had no doubts about its supremacy. 'Whether, then, for the glorious effulgence of its blossoms, which appear to glow like fire in the few sunny hours of the regions it inhabits, or the singular tint its foliage assumes at other seasons, it is one of the most striking plants of the inhospitable regions it inhabits'. Some of Hooker's introductions were planted in the miniature valley at Kew, created a century earlier by Capability Brown, now familiar to visitors as Rhododendron Dell. He encouraged friends living in the coastal belt of the West of Scotland and South-West England to grow them, thereby preparing the way for the ubiquitous woodland garden of the end of the century.

Joseph Hooker's success in Sikkim and the splendid lithographs in his *Rhododendrons of Sikkim–Himalaya* prompted Thomas Nuttall to send his nephew, Thomas Booth, to India in June 1849 to collect them. Booth, unable to get into Sikkim where the imprisonment of Hooker and his companion, Archibald Campbell, had precipitated a political crisis between the Maharaja and the British authorities, explored Assam instead. There on a mountain ridge he found '*R. campylocarpum*, *R. keysii* and *R. hookeri* with leaves curled up like so many Havana cigars and assuming a very wintery appearance'. His discoveries convinced the *Botanical Magazine* that 'if the lofty mountains of the Malayan Archipelago were as well explored, an equally extensive harvest would be reaped' (plate 5002). His most notable introduction, *R. nuttallii* evoked yet another of Sir William's superlatives: 'the finest of all the Rhdodendrons . . . . As *Victoria regia* is justly considered the Queen of Water-lilies, so the plant here represented may with equal justice be called the Prince of Rhododendrons' (plate 5146). Unfortunately, this rhododendron with large rose-tinted white flowers is too tender to survive outside the protection of the greenhouse.

Michael Waterer of the Knap Hill nursery raised the first hybrid when he crossed the two American species, *R. maximum* and *R. catawbiense* in 1810. At Highclere in 1826 the Indian *R. arboreum* was crossed with this hybrid to produce × *altaclerense* on which the *Botanical Magazine* bestowed a folded plate (3423). *R. molle*, newly arrived from China in 1823, became one of the parents of the Mollis hybrids. *R. catawbiense*, *R. caucasicum*, *R. maximum* and *R. ponticum* as proven dependable parents, were crossed with many of the new arrivals from Asia. The nursery of Standish and Noble viewed the Sikkim introductions as 'material for giving new features to succeeding crosses . . ., from *fulgens* and *thomsonii* we shall obtain brilliancy of colour, rivalling even aboreum itself; while *wightii* will contribute a yellow tint, and *hodgsonii* the beautiful form of its individual flowers, as well as that of its fine compact truss'.[3] Robert Fortune's *R. fortunei*, introduced from China in 1855, was quickly greeted by hybridists as yet another

[3] *Gardeners' Chronicle*, 1855.

accommodating parent. As new species flowered, they were subjected to an exacting examination, their qualities were evaluated and if deemed desirable, they were duly crossed, and even the hybrids themselves were crossed to produce a confusing permutation of hardy, reliable and, consequently, popular plants.

Hybridization had started in earnest during the 1820s. William Herbert selected narcissi to prove his theory that some species were, in fact, natural hybrids. At the same time he realized that 'the facility of raising hybrid varieties affords an endless source of interest and amusement'. And, very soon, the crossing of species to obtain hardiness or vigorous growth or exotic blooms became the passion of professional and amateur gardeners. The modern varieties of *Crinum, Gladiolus, Hippeastrum* and *Narcissus* owe much to Herbert's pioneering work. Two of the most skilful Victorian hybridists were employees of the Veitch nursery: John Dominy and John Seden. Dominy excelled with orchids and nepenthes and his pupil, Seden, made his reputation with orchids, begonias and hardy fruit. It was the breeding of so many attractive varieties of calceolarias, zonal geraniums, lobelias, petunias and verbenas that encouraged the fashion of bedding-out.

Through the pages of the *Botanical Magazine* one can detect a slow but progressive interest in alpines. An early example was *Gentiana excisa* (plate 52) in 1788. James Lothian's *Practical hints on the culture and general management of alpine or rock plants* (1845) was written in response to a demand from people who wanted to grow them. Backhouse of York made a speciality of rock plants and in 1865 issued their first catalogue devoted entirely to alpines. The nursery selected their favourites for figuring in the *Botanical Magazine*. 'Thanks, especially to the exertions of the Messrs Backhouse', said the text of *Gentiana pyrenaica*, 'the horticultural-loving public begin to understand the ease and effectiveness with which alpine plants can be cultivated, and the beautiful appearance they make' (plate 5742).

William Robinson thought it fitting to dedicate his *Alpine flowers for English gardens* (1870) to the Backhouse nursery. In this book and *The wild garden*, also published in 1870, he began his crusade against bedding-out. He was a man of prejudice and passion, of strong preferences and violent antipathies. He denounced formal gardens and viewed the glasshouse as an alien intrusion. He was sound in his views on the cultivation of the British flora but silly in his insistence on the usage of English rather than Latin names, even if he had to invent them. He propounded sensible principles for rock gardens and pioneered the herbaceous border and the woodland garden. He championed 'the cause of the innumerable hardy plants against the few tender ones' and urged the naturalization of bulbs in meadow grass 'where they will flourish without further care or cost'. The *Botanical Magazine* praised his books which provided 'a new direction to the energies of those lovers of horticulture who have little time, space or means for gardening' (plate 5924).

Erica mammosa
Royal Botanic Gardens. Kew.

PLATE 26
Erica mammosa. Lilian Snelling. Watercolour. (*Curtis's Botanical Magazine*, vol.
167, 1950, N.S. plate 100). A wide range of colour variation can be found in
this South African erica, from dark red through orange, pink,
purple-pink to white.

~8~

SIR JOSEPH HOOKER

WHEN Sir William Hooker died, his son, Joseph, succeeded him both as Director at Kew and editor of the *Botanical Magazine*. After Lovell Reeve's death, the management of the firm passed to his partner, Francis Lesiter Soper, who could not have been blamed had he jettisoned the Magazine as his first act. However, no change was made to its contents or format and it continued to come out monthly with six plates, 3s.6d. coloured or 2s.6d. plain. As only one complete set from the first volume in 1787 was still available for purchase, the decision was taken to reprint those volumes out of print to complete a few more sets for subscribers.

In the first volume that Joseph Hooker edited, James Bateman, a distinguished orchidologist, described 21 orchids. *Begonia pearcei* (plate 5545) commemorated Richard Pearce who had collected the tuberous-rooted section of the genus in Bolivia and Peru for Veitch. In 1812 the first begonia, *B. evansiana* (plate 1473) from the Far East, appeared in the Magazine although, rather surprisingly, the first species to be cultivated in Britain – *B. nitida* which was sent to Kew from Jamaica in 1777 – was not acknowledged by the *Botanical Magazine* until 1843 when *B. coccinea* was also described. It had been found in the Organ Mountains in Brazil by William Lobb and Sir William Hooker thought it 'unquestionably the most beautiful of the many handsome species of Begonia now known to our collections' (plate 3990). Begonias have an extensive geographical distribution. *B. rex*, for instance, was discovered in Assam and was greeted by Sir William as 'the most lovely of the many lovely species of Begonia' (plate 5101). He regretted the begonia's horticultural merits were not generally appreciated. 'The Begonias are eminently beautiful, both in flower and in leaf;

Sir Joseph Dalton Hooker
(1817–1911).

the latter, especially exhibit a richness and variety of colouring unequalled in almost any other genus of plants; and many new varieties of foliage are obtained by skilful management, which are now reckoned among the most charming of plants for stove cultivation, or, in summer, for a warm greenhouse' (plate 5284). Richard Pearce's *B. boliviensis* (plate 5657) attracted a great deal of admiring attention when it was exhibited at the International Horticultural Show in Paris in 1867. With the skill of the hybridist to exploit its great variety of flower and foliage, the popularity of the begonia as a handsome plant for the conservatory, hall or drawing room was assured. John Seden raised the first tuberous begonia hybrid, using *B. boliviensis* as one of the parents.

In January 1867 Soper reassured Hooker that he had no intention of permitting a decline in the traditional standards of his Magazine. This letter appears to have been in response to a complaint about a deterioration in hand-colouring. 'Last month the colourers were much pressed for time & possibly some of the plates were less carefully done from their having been obliged at this season of short & dark days to work with deficient light'. He revealed to Hooker the delicate financial state of the firm, lamenting that 'it is a slow and difficult process to turn natural history books into cash'.[1]

Up to 1868, with the exception of the orchids which he had delegated to James Bateman, Joseph Hooker had written all the text. Plate 5686 is the first to be signed by another contributor – John Gilbert Baker, then an assistant in the Kew Herbarium, who was to describe most of the Monocotyledons in the Magazine. As a token of appreciation vol. 106 (1880) was dedicated to him; his contributions had reached a total of 250 by the time he submitted his last one in 1903.

In an agreement drawn up between the firm of Lovell Reeve and Joseph Hooker on January 29, 1877, it was stipulated that Hooker would supply drawings and text for which he would be paid £8.13s.4d. for each number. The drawings, after they had been lithographed, would remain the property of the editor. It was a dispute over the ownership of these and earlier drawings, all executed by W. H. Fitch, which was to be the cause of Fitch's severance of relations with the *Botanical Magazine*.

Since 1860 Fitch had experienced the freedom and the insecurity of a freelance artist. As he had a large family to support, he was constantly seeking commissions. In 1874 he offered his services to the Director of the Botanic Garden at Edinburgh. 'I can draw plants from living or dried specimen on stone or wood and should be happy to copy drawings etc. on very moderate terms & can use the microscope'.[2] One regular source of income – the *Botanical Magazine* – was in jeopardy.

He unburdened himself to the botanist, George Bentham, whose *Handbook of the British flora* (1863) he had illustrated. 'I am too old to give up a claim I consider just, & any persistence in it is to prevent what the publisher of the Bot. Mag. has tried to accomplish since 1860 – what a late unfortunate Treasurer of the Linn. Soc. assisted & what, I am loath to believe, the P.R.S. [President of the

[1] Royal Botanic Gardens, Kew. Library (Archives). Item 49, January 8, 1867.
[2] Royal Botanic Garden, Edinburgh. Library (Archives). April 22, 1874.

Royal Society – Joseph Hooker] seems reckless of effecting (legally perhaps) – my ruin. I have drawn for the Bot. Mag. without a hitch for nearly 40 years & it is not likely I may be able to carry on such a work much longer. The drawbacks, the responsibilities & exactions I have had to endure since 1860 have given my nerves such a strain that I feel at times heartsick, not only of the Bot. Mag., but even of Botany & long to get out of a line which I have followed not without credit to myself & I think I may add benefit to your own favourite science'.[3]

The claim Fitch alluded to, was to the ownership of some 1,200 drawings he had done for the *Botanical Magazine* since 1860. Up to that time Sir William Hooker, who had employed him, had placed his drawings in the Kew Herbarium and, according to Fitch's submission to the First Commissioner of the Office of Works,[4] the practice had continued on the understanding that Sir William obtained an official allowance for him. The allowance was never granted and his son, Joseph, never paid him for the drawings he continued to add to the Kew collection. The ownership of these drawings represented a considerable sum of money for Fitch who normally asked two or three guineas for a drawing. Sir Joseph Hooker (he was knighted in 1877) emphatically repudiated the claim. The firm of Lovell Reeve who had paid for all the drawings and therefore reserved the right to dispose of them, had presented them after publication to the editor who, in turn, gave them to Kew. 'Mr Fitch's grievance (if any) is with the publisher of the Magazine, but he has never from 1860, until 1876 when he proposed to leave the publisher's service, claimed any whole or part proprietorship of the drawings, either from the late or present Editor, or from the publisher. Mr Fitch is in error in stating that the late Editor placed any drawings in the Herbarium on the strength of a promise that he would use his best endeavours to get Mr Fitch an official allowance from the Board'.[5] The Office of Works, on advice from Sir Joseph, informed Fitch that since he was not in their employ, they could not participate in the dispute.

Whatever the outcome of this unfortunate affair, Fitch had resolved to cease working for the *Botanical Magazine* and prepared the way by telling Soper that he would like his nephew, F. N. Fitch, to lithograph his drawings because his eyesight was failing. Then there were delays in submitting the drawings. Exasperated, Soper appealed to Sir Joseph. 'Can you furnish me with drawings for the Febr^y Bot. Mag. I cannot induce Fitch to go on as before & must therefore make other arrangements. I consider his lithography quite as essential to the character of the Magazine as his drawings; if we must dispense with one we may as well dispense with the other. Any one competent to lithograph from his sketches, would be equally competent to draw them. If your daughter, Mrs Dyer can furnish the drawings, either protem: or as long as convenient, I will make the best arrangements I can for the lithography'.[6]

[3] Royal Botanic Gardens, Kew. Library (Archives). Bentham letters, vol. 4, item 1444, *c.*May 1876.
[4] *Ibid*, Lovell Reeve: copies of miscellaneous correspondence, January 7, 1879.
[5] *Ibid*, Hooker to the Secretary of the Office of Works, January 29, 1879.
[6] *Ibid*, Lovell Reeve: copies of miscellaneous correspondence, Soper to Hooker, item 58, December 27, 1877.

PLATE 27
Corylus maxima var. *purpurea*. Ann V. Webster. Watercolour. (*Curtis's Botanical Magazine*, vol. 171, 1956, N.S. plate 268). The flowers, leaves and fruit were painted at intervals during the year.

William Thiselton-Dyer, Sir Joseph's son-in-law and his Assistant Director at Kew assured Sir Joseph that his wife, Harriet, would be willing to help with some of the drawings. What also emerges from his letter[7] is the news that Sir Joseph was thinking of resigning as editor. Thiselton-Dyer declined the offer to succeed him, recommending instead Daniel Oliver, Professor of Botany at University College, London. In February 1878 Soper asked Thiselton-Dyer to tell his wife to colour some prints as patterns for the colourists; her first signed drawings appeared in the March issue. Still looking for a permanent replacement for Fitch, Soper proposed Miss E. Regel who had drawn some plates for the *Florist and Pomologist*; another candidate was Miss Olsen, currently employed as an artist by Professor Richard Owen but with little experience of botanical drawing.

Fitch viewed the efforts of the 'scratch pack', as he called it, with contempt. In the meanwhile he consulted William Carruthers, Keeper of the Department of Botany at the British Museum, about the feasibility of resurrecting the *Botanical Register*. Ridgway, the original publisher, seemed to be interested in the proposal. One cannot help thinking that behind this suggestion which never progressed any further was Fitch's desire to get even with the *Botanical Magazine*. It is sad that the botanical artist who so epitomized the spirit of the Victorian era, its industry, vitality and self-confidence, should have ended his days an embittered man.

Nearly 10,000 of his drawings were published, including most of those emanating from Kew, over a period of 40 years. Lithography proved to be a perfect medium for his spontaneous and rapid method of working. His skill in conjuring up a plant portrait from dried specimens was put to the test in illustrating the botanical results of the *Erebus* and *Terror* expedition to Antarctica in 1839–43. All his work is characterized by a vigorous boldness, expressed in firm but loosely drawn lines and rich colouring. Although the painstaking detail associated with botanical drawing is absent from much of his work, his acute visual memory and thorough botanical knowledge enabled him to capture the quintessential qualities of a plant. Sir Joseph, never an easy man to please, admitted, 'I don't think Fitch *could* make a mistake in his perspective and outline, not even if he tried'. W. Botting Hemsley, who often watched Fitch at work, described his methods. 'In a standing position, with a block in one hand and a pencil in the other, he drew without hesitation, and with a rapidity and dexterity that was simply marvellous. The lilies [for H. J. Elwes's *Genus Lilium*] he drew also in a standing position direct on the stone, which was posed, at a slight angle. The bold freehand lines were laid on with an unerring sweep of the pencil. This was in 1880, when he was no longer in his prime'.[8] His fantastic output and the remarkable fluency of his pencil have suggested to some critics a lack of sensitivity amounting almost to a mechanical perfection in his work. There are those, too, who question the quality of his colouring which was bold without fussy detailing, yet so easy for the colourists to copy. Sir Joseph acknowledged Fitch as one 'who by his artistic talents contributed so largely to

[7] Royal Botanic Gardens, Kew. Library (Archives). item 19, February 19, 1878.

[8] *Kew Bulletin*, 1915, p. 278.

the value of my father's work'. When the last plate with his name was published in the October 1878 issue, he had submitted about 2,900 drawings to the Magazine. Sir Joseph who had dedicated vol. 95 to him was instrumental in obtaining for him in 1880 a Civil List pension of £100 a year. Fitch was moved by this kind gesture and consideration. In thanking Sir Joseph, he expressed the wish that 'our misunderstanding (which I sincerely regret) has left no doubt on your mind of my respect for yourself as I had for your father'.[9]

The years immediately following Fitch's departure were difficult ones for the editor whose family rallied to his aid; his daughter Harriet Thiselton-Dyer, his sister-in-law Mrs Anne Barnard, and his cousin Matilda Smith, drew the plates with a touching devotion. Additional assistance came from the artistic talents of Misses E. A. Ormerod and P. H. Woolward and Messrs F. Burbidge, N. E. Brown, W. W. Saunders and W. G. Smith. To ease the difficulty in recruiting

Matilda Smith (1854–1926).

artists Soper increased the rate of payment to 15s. for each drawing inclusive of the coloured pattern print.

In 1886 and for the next 34 years most of the plates were drawn by Matilda Smith, trained by Sir Joseph himself. Flower painting had always been accepted as an elegant occupation for ladies, especially those who suffered from a surfeit of leisure. The creative activities of the Victorian woman were constricted by the social conventions of her time, but the gentle indulgence in painting or collecting curious shells or pressing plants was considered to elevate the mind as well as to sharpen the perceptions. Drawing masters were much in demand, and when the talents of their pupils could not cope with portraiture or landscape, there was always the less demanding skills (so it was believed) of flower painting to be taught. Indeed it was generally accepted, with notable exceptions, that women were better than men at flower painting. 'The treatment of flowers requires that fine and delicate feeling, in which ladies excel men, rather than the powerful mastery of a great artist'.[10] The great eighteenth-century botanical artist, Georg

---

[9] Royal Botanic Gardens, Kew. Library (Archives), item 7, April 16, 1880.
[10] E. Braun, *Explanatory text and additional plates to Lewis Grunet's specimens of ornamental art*, 1850.

Ehret, prospered by teaching flower drawing to wives and daughters of the gentry. Even Queen Charlotte and her daughters sought instruction from Kew's artist, Francis Bauer. A few examples of the work of two accomplished women artists can be seen in the early volumes of the *Botanical Magazine*: Mrs Clara Maria Pope and Mrs Augusta Withers. Mrs Pope gave drawing lessons and exhibited at the Royal Academy. Samuel Curtis used her talents in his *Beauties of Flora* and *Monograph on the Genus Camellia*. Mrs Withers became Painter of Flowers to Queen Adelaide, but Matilda Smith was never in that class. Like her illustrious predecessor, W. H. Fitch, she was skilled in recreating a plant from dried specimens. Her artistic talents, it must be confessed, did not rise above average competency, and she was fortunate to have much of her work translated into lithography by the very capable John Nugent Fitch.

The departure of W. H. Fitch meant also the loss of his ability as a lithographer and the *Botanical Magazine* was not to enjoy that successful marriage of skills until the appointment of Lilian Snelling many years later. Whoever replaced Fitch as a lithographer had to have the capacity to collaborate with the artist, to interpret line, brush stroke and meticulous detail with a constant fidelity. John Nugent Fitch, trained by his critical uncle, was an obvious candidate for the post. He lithographed nearly 2,500 plates and certainly Matilda Smith's drawings benefitted from his sympathetic lithographic transformation. He was an artists in his own right in the 11 volumes of Warner and Williams's *Orchid album* (1882–97). His original sketches for this work are reminiscent of similar documentation by W. H. Fitch – rough pencil outlines with indicative washes of colour.

One of the less pleasant tasks given to Miss Smith was painting the giant aroid, *Amorphophallus titanum*. It had been collected by the Italian botanist, Odoardo Beccari in West Sumatra in 1878 and seedlings sent to Kew. One plant outgrowing its accommodation in the Aroid house was transferred to the *Victoria amazonica* house where it continued to grow alarmingly, thrusting its stalk triumphantly up to 2.4 m (8 ft) by 1888. As it approached its brief triumph of flowering the rate of growth accelerated. 'By June 5th [1889] the top of the spathe pushed through the sheath; after which the inflorescence grew in height about three inches a day, and reached its full development on June 21st. Its ultimate height was six feet nine inches. The peduncle was eighteen inches high, the spathe three feet long and four feet across the mouth, and the spadix five feet long by ten inches in diameter at the thickest part above the flower' (plates 7153–55). It was the first time it had flowered in Europe. Miss Smith resolutely endured its offensive smell, 'a mixture of rotten fish and burnt sugar', covered with a veil of flies, in order to record it for the *Botanical Magazine*. It is not surprising that she was subsequently ill. The smell from *Amorphophallus oncophyllus* which flowered some years later at Kew was even more disgusting and 'visitors rushed through the "Begonia house" in which it was exhibited, to escape from it' (plate 7327).

Three plates were allocated to *A. titanum* in the 1891 volume of the Magazine which also reported another unusual flowering. A seemingly dead trunk of *Yucca australis* (plate 7197) from Monterey in California was put on display in the

Amorpholphallus titanum (plate 7153). Left: Drawing by Matilda Smith;
Right: Photograph taken at Kew Gardens on 21 June 1889.

Museum of Economic Botany at Kew in 1888. Two years later rudimentary leaves and a flower appeared and, on being transferred to the Temperate House, it responded by a splendid display of long panicles of white flowers.

1891 was also notable for another event: the purchase from Caroline Curtis of nearly 1,700 original *Botanical Magazine* drawings by Sydenham Edwards, James Sowerby, John Curtis and others for the extremely modest sum of £50.[11] During the 1890s Soper tried to reduce his large stock of plates of the Magazine by offering them at 6d. or 1s. each.

In 1903, Sir Joseph Hooker, now in his eighty-seventh year, realized that he could no longer carry on the editorship single-handed. He turned to William Botting Hemsley, the Principal Assistant in the Kew Herbarium to whom he had dedicated vol. 124 (1898), for help. Believing that the firm of Lovell Reeve would be reluctant to see his name removed from the title page, he asked Botting Hemsley whether he would write the descriptions under his own name. He also wondered 'whether the descriptions & descriptive matter have not become too laboured for what is after all, more a book for Gardening & Amateurs than for purely scientific botanists, comparatively few of whom consult it & these chiefly for the Plates'.[12] Botting Hemsley readily agreed but foresaw difficulties with the Director at Kew, Sir William Thiselton-Dyer, whom, he believed, wanted to turn it into a semi-official publication. He also feared that the Director would not work amicably with the firm of Lovell Reeve. No doubt with Sir William's

[11] Royal Botanic Gardens, Kew. Library (Archives). Kew Herbarium presentations to 1900, vol. 1, item 210–16.
[12] *Ibid*, Lovell Reeve: copies of miscellaneous correspondence, item 15(1), July 15, 1903.

autocratic and difficult personality in mind, Botting Hemsley warned Sir Joseph that 'it would be suicidal for any member of the [Kew] staff to act independently of the Director. Of course, if he would agree to my becoming editor eventually it would give me great honour to undertake it'.[13] As editor, Botting Hemsley said he would invite contributions from his colleagues at Kew. Sir Joseph informed Soper that he could no longer edit the Magazine unaided, that Botting Hemsley was his choice as an assistant editor, and that he would welcome an increase in his salary to meet the expense of having to pay Botting Hemsley.[14]

In his reply Soper, a fellow octogenarian, reminded Sir Joseph that when he had joined Lovell Reeve in 1862 the circulation of the Magazine had been about 350; its decline to 235 in 1903 was barely sufficient to cover the cost of production. He had resisted suggestions to close the Third Series which some thought too large for new subscribers because he wanted it to be the Hooker series – 'a noble monument of scientific industry to Father and Son'.[15] He would like vol. 130 for which some of the drawings had already been done to be completed under Sir Joseph's auspices. He agreed to Botting Hemsley's appointment and to his name appearing on the monthly wrappers and the title page. Botting Hemsley pressed Hooker for his name to go on the wrappers immediately 'because if I do not get it on under your influence I do not believe I shall get it on at all'.[16] His name was added to the title pages of vols. 129 (1903) and 130 (1904) but, as he had predicted, Sir William Thiselton-Dyer objected. 'I confess I was very much surprised', Sir William told Soper, 'when the editorship was placed in the hands of one of my subordinates'.[17]

Sir Joseph contributed only three descriptions and a joint one with Botting Hemsley to his last volume in 1904; most were written by Botting Hemsley and the remainder by members of the Kew staff. And for the first time since 1868, Sir Joseph relinquished the pleasure of describing his beloved orchids.

During the long span of years that Sir Joseph was editor, much more of the world's flora had been discovered and carried back to Europe. His own discoveries in India had brought that subcontinent to prominence in the pages of the *Botanical Magazine*. In neighbouring Burma the Rev. Charles Parish and Colonel Robson Benson gave every spare moment to orchids. The small gathering of Afghan flowers came from J. E. T. Aitchison while he was naturalist on the Afghanistan Delimitation Commission. Far to the north of Afghanistan, in Turkestan, Albert Regel, serving in the Russian Imperial Army, sent plants to his father, the Director of the Botanical Gardens at St Petersburg. Dr Edward Regel to whom vol. 111 of the Magazine was dedicated, generously presented Kew with bulbs and seeds from his son's collections. Volume after volume from 1879 acknowledged Albert Regel's industry. The quantity of irises coming from the region caused Hooker to speculate that Central Asia was probably the home of the genus.

[13] *Ibid*, item 10, July 17, 1903.
[14] *Ibid*, item 17, July 21, 1903.
[15] *Ibid*, Sir Joseph Hooker letters, item 69, July 27, 1903.
[16] *Ibid*, Sir Joseph Hooker letters, item 13, August 14, 1903.
[17] *Ibid*, October 15, 1904.

George Maw, an authority on crocuses, planted a representative collection in Kew Gardens from his own collections made in Southern Europe and North Africa. In dedicating the Magazine to him in 1874, Sir Joseph was reminded of the botanical excursion he, Maw and John Ball had made to the Great Atlas Mountains of Morocco in 1871. Several volumes feature plants collected by the trio on that occasion. At the southern tip of the African continent, the Cape flora continued to excite the attention of collectors such as Thomas Cooper and John Medley Wood, the Curator of the Durban Garden. Gustav Mann was responsible for many of the plants from West Africa and the island of Fernando Po. G. F. Scott-Elliot on the French and English Delimitation Commission of the Sierra Leone Boundary more than adequately filled his official role as botanist. John Kirk, David Livingstone's companion on his second expedition, during his consular duties in Zanzibar collected widely in East Africa. It was also in East Africa that Baron Walter von Saint Paul-Illaine collected the seed of the African violet named after him, *Saintpaulia ionantha* (plate 7408). Within a couple of years of its flowering it was exhibited at the International Horticultural Exhibition in Ghent in 1893 and was figured in five horticultural periodicals. The destruction of the habitat of this popular house plant through agricultural development and the uncontrolled activities of collectors have threatened its survival in the wild. It was the first plant to be selected for the regular 'Plants in peril' feature in the *Kew Magazine*, the successor to the *Botanical Magazine* which had greeted it so enthusiastically nearly a century earlier.

Right up to the end of the nineteenth century the paramount role of the American flora was never seriously questioned. During the 40 years he was editor, Sir Joseph selected 178 plants from North America, 142 from Brazil, 103 from Colombia, 89 from Mexico with Peru, Chile, Venezuela, Ecuador and the West Indies extending the geographical panorama.

New Australian plants, on the other hand, no longer had the attention of British gardeners. Without the offerings of Sir Frederick Mueller, the Director of the Melbourne Botanical Garden, their representation in the Magazine would have been slight. One wonders whether Sir Joseph had a fondness for *Veronica* (now *Hebe*), the New Zealand shrub, since he described 14 species.

Henry Ridley's appointment as Director of the Botanical Garden at Singapore in 1888 began a steady flow of plants to Kew. Charles Curtis, a former Veitch collector, as Superintendent of the Gardens at Penang, was another donor. The little-known flora of New Guinea was being explored and new species of *Dendrobium* were identified.

The defeat of the Chinese in the first Opium War of 1840–42 breached their xenophobic isolation. Europeans were no longer confined to a few coastal ports; through enforced treaties they got access to the Chinese interior. Missionaries working in central and western China studied the local flora and fauna. The greatest of these amateur naturalists was Father Jean Pierre Armand David, commemorated in *Davidia involucrata*, the 'paper handkerchief' tree which he discovered. Another French missionary, Father Jean Delavay found new species of rhododendrons, gentians and lilies in South-West China. Fathers Jean Soulié and Paul Farges botanized in Sichuan. The *Botanical Magazine* reflected the excitement generated by the floral wealth of the East. Charles Ford, Super-intendent of the Botanical and Afforestation Department of Hong Kong, supplied many of the 80 Chinese plants illustrated between 1865 and 1899; the five volumes covering 1900 to 1904 have 35 plants – a sudden increase which heralded the beginning of Chinese dominance.

By 1904 the Magazine had described about 30 species of primulas; during the following 50 years no fewer than 60 new species, mainly from the Far East, would be figured. This genus includes some of the best-loved garden plants: *Primula japonica* which its discoverer, Robert Fortune, dubbed 'Queen of Primroses' (plate 5916); *P. sikkimensis*, 'the pride of all the alpine Primulas' (plate 4597); and *P. sinensis* (plate 7559), first made known through a drawing sent to London by John Reeves.

In his last year as Director, Sir Joseph received the offer of plants from Augustine Henry, a Customs official in China; before he left China in 1900 Henry had sent Kew over 25 new genera and 500 species mainly as herbarium specimens. One of his few garden introductions was the orange-coloured *Lilium henryi* (plate 7177) which he had found growing in the limestone cliffs along the Yangtse River in Hubei. His achievements were overshadowed by his successors, in particular E. H. Wilson who is mentioned in the *Botanical Magazine* for the first time in 1903.

As Director of one of the world's foremost botanical gardens, Sir Joseph had no difficulty in finding plants suitable for the Magazine. He was, nevertheless, grateful for small contributions from the Cambridge, Dublin, Edinburgh and Glasgow botanical gardens.

Veitch, William Bull of Chelsea and William Thompson of Ipswich were prominent amongst nurserymen donors; Backhouse of York was always a dependable source of interesting alpines.

Many flowers came from the Gloucestershire garden of J. H. Elwes, 'traveller, collector and observing naturalist' (plate 6166). The treasures of some of the finest gardens in the country were at Sir Joseph's disposal: Belgrove (W. E. Gumbleton), Bentall Hall (G. Maw), Bitton Rectory (Rev. H. Ellacombe), Burford Lodge (Sir Trevor Lawrence), Hay Lodge (J. Anderson-Henry), Heatherbank (G. F. Wilson), Hillfield (W. W. Saunders), Knypersley (J. Bateman), Leonardslee (E. G. Loder), Munstead (G. Jekyll), Pendell Court (Sir George Macleay), Warley Place (E. Willmott) and Wimbledon Park (G. Joad). All made contributions to the *Botanical Magazine*; even Sir Thomas Hanbury despatched a few flowers from his exotic garden at La Mortala in northern Italy.

Sir Joseph Hooker, always imaginative in his choice of plants, never hesitated to portray a few that had no decorative appeal whatsoever – the fodder grass, *Euchlaena mexicana* (plate 6414), for example. He extended his range to include *Hypolytrum latifolium*, the 'graceful green foliage, rich brown inflorescence and . . . permanent freshness' of this member of Cyperaceae he deemed 'well worthy of cultivation in a tropical house' (plate 6282).

He saw his role as a fashioner of horticultural taste. 'The Botanical Magazine claims the privilege of figuring, from time to time, plants which are not as yet in cultivation in England, but which are so remarkable for their interest or beauty as to be objects of great and special interest, and to which public attention should be drawn' (plate 5607). He believed that 'the Botanical Magazine has no higher function than that of figuring such plants as are rarely known to flower in this country and are so difficult of preservation for scientific purposes, or for future identification, that but for good coloured plates, they can scarcely ever be recognized' (plate 5940). He put agaves, aloes and palms in this category; when the South American palm, *Scheelia Kewensis*, flowered in the Palm House at Kew he thought the rare event deserved two plates (plates 7552–53).

Subscribers had fewer economic plants, the most noteworthy was probably *Cinchona calisaya* (plate 6434), the source of quinine. *Typhonium brownii* (plate 6180) had little commercial value, but Sir Joseph justified its inclusion because of its 'great scientific interest'.

Hybrids seldom met with his editorial approval, believing as he did 'that it is the more legitimate function of a Botanical work to illustrate the possible or probable parents of future hybrids, and thus afford to others the means of elucidating the history of hybrids when these are formed' (plate 6058). But he made an exception of *Nymphaea* × *kewensis* which had attracted so many visitors to the water-lily house at Kew.

It had always been the practice of the Magazine to include English names of plants, even if this meant translating the Latin form. As few of them were genuine or widely accepted, Sir Joseph very sensibly omitted them from 1871. In 1883 a *General index to the Latin names and synonyms of the plants depicted in the first 107 volumes* was published; it also included a short list of popular names.

With Sir Joseph Hooker's resignation as editor in 1904, there came to an end an association between the Hooker family and the *Botanical Magazine* that had lasted for 77 years. Through them the firm of Lovell Reeve had enjoyed privileged access to the unrivalled resources of the Royal Botanic Gardens at Kew. Without that connection and the reputation of impeccable authority that the name of the Hookers conferred, it is likely that the Magazine would have followed its competitors into bankruptcy and extinction.

PLATE 28
Edithcolea grandis. Margaret Stones. Watercolour. (*Curtis's Botanical Magazine*, vol.
177, 1970, N.S. plate 562). Named after Miss Edith Cole who discovered it in
British Somaliland about 1895.

9

ORCHIDOMANIA

No other family of plants can match orchids for a virtuoso display of bizarre shapes and subtle colouring. The names of many of the genera indicate the extraordinary diversity of form the flower can take: *Coryanthes* (helmet flower), *Cymbidium* (boat-shaped), *Odontoglossum* (tooth-tongued), or *Phalaenopsis* (moth-like). Some have an overpowering fragrance like that of the *Stanhopea*; many, surprisingly, have no scent at all and the offensive odour of an unfortunate few like *Bulbophyllum beccarii* keeps admirers at a discreet distance. These aristocrats of the plant kingdom, numbering between 15,000 and 30,000 species can be found in most countries, even in the inhospitable Arctic. Most flourish happily in the tropical and sub-tropical regions of the world: from the rain forests of Central and South America, along the Sino-Himalayan range to the islands of Borneo, New Guinea and the Philippines. They grow on the ground, on outcrops of rock and on the extended branches of tall trees. Aerial orchids, or epiphytes, thrive in humid forests, trailing their roots in space. This peculiarity was not fully understood by early growers and few epiphytes survived their inexpert attempts to cultivate them. Philip Miller whose *Gardener's dictionary* enumerated several species of *Epidendrum* confessed that 'the plants cannot by any art yet known be cultivated in the ground'. He potted three of them, put them in a stove where 'they came so far as to show their flowers, but the plants soon afterwards perished'.

To Sir Charles Wager of Fulham must go the honour of flowering the first tropical orchid in England. It was a *Bletia* from the Bahamas, given to him by his friend Peter Collinson in 1731; it survived the customary potting treatment but presumably soon died after putting on a brave show of colour. About 1778 Mrs Hird of Appleby Bridge in Yorkshire managed to coax a Chinese *Phaius tankervilleae*, given to her by her uncle John Fothergill, to produce bold spikes of purplish flowers. This species was illustrated in William Aiton's *Hortus Kewensis* (1789) which lists 15 foreign orchids including *Encyclia fragrans* and *E. cochleata*, both successfully flowered at Kew. Twenty-four years later, the second edition of *Hortus Kewensis* recorded 115 species, three-quarters of them exotics from the West and East Indies, the Cape and Australia.

The high casualty rate did not deter growers from persevering with traditional methods of cultivation. In 1810 the *Botanical Magazine* reported that E. J. A. Woodford's gardener recommended that cypripediums 'should be placed in a shady position in the bark stove, the roots should be protected with knobs of old tan and only sparingly watered, but the air should be kept hot and damp'. In 1812, the year in which William Roxburgh, Superintendent of the Botanical Garden at Calcutta, despatched the first Indian *Aerides, Dendrobium*

Cattleya labiata (plate 3998).
W. H. Fitch. Engraved by J. Swan.

and *Vanda*, Conrad Loddiges's nursery at Hackney began cultivating orchids in earnest and soon became the country's principal supplier. They illustrated many of their orchids in their periodical, *Botanical Cabinet*.

Cattleya labiata (plate 3998) was the first orchid to attract the envy of collectors. William Swainson is supposed to have used it to pack around plants he had collected on the Organ Mountains in Brazil and William Cattley, out of curiosity, planted this fortuitous packing in his hothouse. He is credited with its first flowering in 1818 but Sir Joseph Hooker also claimed that distinction for Sir William Hooker.[1] As, however, John Lindley named the plant in honour of Cattley, Sir Joseph's claim is questionable. Its flamboyant rose-coloured flowers became the pride of privileged collections, but its habitat remained unknown until George Gardner came across it on the Gavea Mountain near Rio. Unfortunately destroyed through indiscriminate deforestation, it was to be another 50 years before it was rediscovered in Pernambuco by one of Sander's collectors.

The Horticultural Society of London built up a collection of epiphytes in order to determine a successful method of cultivating them. The results of these experiments enabled John Lindley, their Assistant Secretary, to present in 1830 a paper *Upon the cultivation of epiphytes of the orchis tribe*, the first time that orchid culture had been scientifically considered.

[1] *Annals of Botany*, vol. 16, 1902, p. xciii.

PLATE 29

Iris iberica subsp. *lycotis*. Mary Grierson. Watercolour. (*Curtis's Botanical Magazine*, vol. 178, 1970, N.S. plate 580). One of the many plants collected by the late Admiral J. P. W. Furse. It has been found in Azerbaidhjan and neighbouring western Iran.

William George Spencer Cavendish, sixth Duke of Devonshire from whom the Horticultural Society of London leased their garden at Chiswick, admired a *Psychopsis papilio* at one of their horticultural shows in 1833. He succumbed to its charms, became an orchid enthusiast and sent John Gibson to India to collect them. Gibson did not disappoint him; when he returned in 1837 his cases were filled with new species of *Dendrobium, Phaius, Vanda, Coelogyne* and *Saccolabium*. The Duke paid a hundred guineas for a white *Phalaenopsis* collected by Hugh Cuming in the Philippines. Presumably he also acquired some of the orchids sent from Guatemala by Skinner, from British Guiana by Schomburgk and from Mexico by Hartweg. 1837 was a very good year for orchids – about 300 new species were delivered to Britain.

In 1839 Loddiges published the first of its orchid lists with over 1,600 species and varieties but their supremacy was threatened by Knight's Exotic Nursery in Chelsea after it had purchased the collections of Cattley and Mrs Arnold Harrison. There were now many growers, wealthy enough to pay the prices prize specimens were commanding. Seventeen pounds was not unusual for single Guatemalan orchids in a sale at Stevens' Auction Rooms in 1846. In London, the principal growers were the Duke of Northumberland, Baron Dimsdale, Mr Harris, Mr Rucker and Mrs Lawrence; in Liverpool, Mr Horsfall and Mr Moss; in Manchester, Mr Wanklyn, Mr Bow and the Rev. John Clowes who bequeathed his collection to Kew and received a grateful acknowledgement in the *Botanical Magazine*'s dedication in 1846.

James Bateman, the most eminent of all the collectors and cultivators, noted with satisfaction that an epiphyte house had become 'an almost indispensible adjunct to a place of any consideration'. His collecting mania had started in his student days at Oxford when Mr Fairburn, a local nurseryman, showed him *Renanthera coccinea* with several stout roots firmly attached to pieces of wood. The *Botanical Magazine* was consulted for a drawing of it. 'It was certainly a vision of beauty that Mr Fairburn, opening a volume of the *Botanical Magazine* t.2997–2998 showed me, for here was a perfect portrait of the Chinese air plant, full size and correctly coloured. Of course I fell in love at first sight, and as Mr F. only asked a guinea for his plant (high prices were not yet in vogue) it soon changed hands and travelled with me to Knypersley, when the Christmas holidays began. I had caught my Orchid, but how to treat it I knew not'.[2] Impatient to possess more new species which were known to be hidden in the American jungles, he engaged Thomas Colley, a foreman at Fairburn's nursery, in 1833 to go to Brazil. Colley's haul was disappointing, only about 20 new orchids. In 1834, Bateman wrote to George Ure Skinner, a merchant trading in Guatemala but also a collector of birds and insects, suggesting that he turned his attention to orchids. Within 10 years some of the finest orchids of that country were flowering at Knypersley. In all, Skinner added almost 100 new species to cultivation. The *Botanical Magazine* repeatedly praised his achievements: *Schomburgkia superbiens*, which Skinner found growing in the crevices of rock, 'of all gorgeous plants deserves the name of superbiens' (plate 4090); *Rossioglossum grande*, 'among the most magnificent ornaments of the Orchidaceous Flora

[2] J. Veitch, *Manual of orchidaceous plants*, 1894, part 10, p. 130.

of Guatemala' (plate 3955); and *Lycaste skinneri* – 'this beautiful plant is of easy cultivation, and thrives in the cool division of the Orchidaceous house' (plate 4445).

Some of Bateman's favourites were drawn for his elephant folio, *The Orchidaceae of Mexico and Guatemala* (1837–43). The bookseller, H. G. Bohn, called it 'the most splendid botanical work of the present age'; without question it is the biggest botanical book of any age. One hundred and twenty-five copies were for subscribers who included fellow orchid enthusiasts – the Liverpool merchants Charles Horsfall and John Moss, the Rev. John Clowes, Mrs Louisa Lawrence and, of course, the Loddiges nursery. The life-size drawings, the majority of which were by Mrs Withers and Miss Drake, are reputed to have cost £200 each to reproduce. On this monumental scale the lithographs could not be other than impressive; and the hand-colouring is immaculate. When Sir William Hooker dedicated a volume of the *Botanical Magazine* to Bateman, he found it impossible to decide whether 'the beauty of the subjects represented, the execution of the figures, or the taste and judgment displayed in the typographical department, is most to be admired' in this magnificent book.

Incipient orchidomania was looming. When growers could not get all they wanted in the London orchid auctions they sent out their own gardeners as collectors. Mr Rucker of Wandsworth and the Rev. John Clowes commissioned Jean Linden to look for orchids in Venezuela and Colombia. It was not unusual for a zealous grower to fill several ranges of glasshouses with them; pots were specially designed for displaying them; horticultural societies offered prizes; in the meanwhile former favourites like camellias and proteas languished. John Lindley's *Folia Orchidacea* (1852–55) recognized the existence of more than 6,000 species.

John Lindley, an industrious official of the Horticultural Society of London and Professor of Botany at University College relaxed – if such a word could ever be applicable to him – by studying orchids. He featured several orchids in *Collectanea botanica* (1821) and the orchid content of the *Botanical Register* expanded enormously after he became its editor. His association with orchids was a life-long love affair resulting in several authoritative works. *Genera and species of Orchidaceous plants* (1830–40) and *Illustrations of Orchidaceous plants* (1830–38) were followed by *Sertum Orchidaceum* (1838–41), an imperial folio which inevitably lacks the dimensions and grandeur of Bateman's work. His outstanding service was to bring some semblance of order and system to the bewildering number of orchids now in cultivation.

The first orchid William Curtis selected for his *Botanical Magazine* – *Calopogon pulchellum* – was given to him by a friend who explained that on 'examining attentively the bog-earth which had been brought over with some plants of the Dionaea muscipula, [he] found tooth-like knobby roots, which, being placed in the pots of the same earth, and plunged into a tan-pit having a gentle heat, produced plants the ensuing summer, two of which have flowered' (plate 116). From such comment in the Magazine and also in the *Botanical Register*, it is apparent that no distinction was ever made between the cultivation of terrestrial

W. W. Saunder's orchid house at Hillfield near Reigate, Surrey.
(*Gardeners' Chronicle*, 1872, p. 1559).

and epiphytic orchids; all were indiscriminately potted in mould composed of decayed leaves and wood, or a mixture of peat and loam, and plunged into the tan bed. Loddiges's orchid house, heated to a high temperature by brick flues with a tan bed kept steamy by watering, was held to be a model by other growers. Loddiges had not grasped the significance of the report of an *Oncidium* from Uruguay continually flowering on the voyage, hung up in a cabin without any earth.

The first tentative steps in the right direction were taken when the gardener at Claremont in Surrey flowered *Aërides odorata* in 1813 by suspending it in a basket of tan and moss. Sir Joseph Banks at Spring Grove, Hounslow hung his epiphytes in cylindrical wicker baskets; William Herbert inserted his orchids into moss-filled notches in branches of trees. In the early 1820s Kew placed their orchids on a bed of loose soil mixed with fragments of branches and twigs.

At the Horticultural Society's garden, John Lindley was trying to improve upon the current methods of cultivation. Unfortunately, he made the wrong deductions when he learnt from the Society's collectors in Brazil that orchids 'exclusively occupy damp woods'. He assumed that a combination of high temperature, humidity and deep shade were essential. His recommendations were unquestioningly adopted by growers who, nevertheless, continued to lose their plants, and as Sir Joseph Hooker observed many years later, England had become 'the grave of tropical orchids; of the millions imported but a few hundred survive the first few years, and this is very much because every collector forms a miscellaneous collection, wherein it is impossible to meet the requirements of any but the most indifferent to the treatment the generality may experience' (plate 6152). Allan Cunningham told Lindley that orchids in Australia grew under conditions completely different from those imposed on them in England. Skinner and William Lobb warned against the practice of subjecting orchids from a temperate zone to the stifling heat of a hothouse, but no-one heeded them.

After Sir William Hooker had seen Lord FitzWilliam's orchids at Wentworth in Yorkshire, he told readers of the *Botanical Magazine* that 'the sight of this collection, whether the vigorous growth and beauty of the foliage, or the number of splendid species blossoming at one time to be considered, far exceeded my warmest anticipations' (plate 3395). Joseph Cooper, the Earl's gardener, had achieved this remarkable result by growing them at lower temperatures and with plenty of fresh air. In 1840 Sir William published an extract of a letter from Donald Beaton who looked after Mr Harris's orchids at Kingsbury in North London. 'I believe this will be the first notice of plants of this tribe [*Laelia*] having been subjected to a cold temperature in this country; and I have ample proof that these and many others will not do so well if they are subjected to a heat above 50° to 55° [F] in winter. Nothing can be more more difficult than to bring some of the plants in my list to a state of healthy growth in our excessively-heated Orchideous houses; but, treated as greenhouse plants, and with a little forcing for six weeks at the end of Spring, or whenever they show a disposition to new growth, they seem as easy to manage as the Stanhopeas' (plate 3804).

It was becoming abundantly clear, when dendrobiums languished where stanhopeas flourished or bletias perished where eulophias and zygopetalums prospered, that each genus might need a different cultural treatment. The *Botanical Magazine* recommended that *Epidendrum cooperianum* from Brazil should be grown in the Mexican House. 'The Cattleya house itself frequently proves too warm and too moist for many of the orchids from the higher portions of the Organ Mountains, whence not a few of the more popular species have come to us' (plate 5654). At Chatsworth, Joseph Paxton put orchids from different climates in separate houses or compartments. John Lindley and everyone who visited the Duke of Devonshire's estate were impressed. 'The success with which the epiphytes are cultivated by Mr Paxton is wonderful, and the climate in which this is effected, instead of being so hot and damp that the plants can only be seen with as much peril as if one had to visit them in an Indian jungle, is as mild and delightful as that of Madeira'.[3] At last it was recognized that certain genera like, for example, *Pleione*, which are now grown in alpine houses or on a window sill, prefer a cool environment. The ingredients for healthy growth were the regulation of temperature, liberal ventilation, and the replacement of brick flues and tan beds by hot water pipes in lighter houses. Benjamin Williams, one of the most talented orchid growers of his day, elaborated this new approach in a series of articles in the *Gardeners' Chronicle* in 1851 entitled 'Orchids for the million'. These formed the basis of his *Orchid grower's manual* (1852) which had become a classic by the time it reached its seventh edition in 1894.

By the mid-nineteenth century the first influx of orchid introductions was coming to an end. Those already in cultivation were being selected as parents of new varieties. Veitch's hybridizer, John Dominy, crossed *Calanthe masuca* and *C. furcata* and when the resultant hybrid, *Calanthe × dominyi* bloomed in 1856, Sir William Hooker had it drawn for the *Botanical Magazine* (plate 5042); he also included *Calanthe × veitchii* (plate 5375), perhaps Dominy's most popular cultivar. Before he retired in 1880 Dominy had 25 hybrids to his credit; his successor, John Seden, achieved over 500. Lindley had wondered whether orchids could produce natural hybrids and it was Seden who proved that they do. Despite his ruling to omit hybrids, Sir Joseph Hooker felt compelled to present the natural hybrid, *Cattleya × whitei*. 'So great has been the interest shown by Orchidologists in the natural hybrid here figured, that I have yielded to their wish that it should appear in the *Botanical Magazine*, as one of the few exceptions to the rule which excludes hybrids in favour of the species, so long as these are pressing for illustration' (plate 7727).

For some 15 years only Veitch attempted hybridization, but as techniques were perfected other growers were encouraged to experiment and new cultivated varieties multiplied, often to be preferred to the species from which they had been bred. The absence of any systematic and reliable record of their parentage prompted the Sander nursery in 1895 to compile a register of hybrids, and in 1906 to publish their first list of orchid hybrids. In 1961 the Royal Horticultural Society assumed the role of an International Registration Authority for orchid cultivators and the maintenance of the lists started by Sander.

[3] *Botanical Register*, vol. 24, 1838.

In 1864 descriptions of seven dendrobiums, all collected by the Rev. Charles Parish in Burma, were published in the *Botanical Magazine*. During the 20 years he was chaplain at Moulmein, he collected orchids, grew some 150 species in his garden, examined them under a microscope, drew them and sent boxes of them to Kew and Hugh Low at Clapton. Sir Joseph Hooker dedicated vol. 96 to him, in recognition of his 'botanical discoveries, especially of orchids, in the Eastern Peninsula of India'. His friend, Colonel Robson Benson of the Burmese Public Works Department, was another enthusiastic orchidologist. Both were amateurs whose commendable efforts considerably swelled the importation of new species but the main source of supply was still the professional collector.

Frederick Burbidge, trained in the gardens of the Royal Horticultural Society and Kew, went to Borneo in 1877 on behalf of James Veitch and Sons. With Peter Veitch, who joined him there, they explored Mount Kinabalu where Hugh Low some 20 years earlier had been delighted by the profusion of orchids and pitcher plants. They brought back the large *Nepenthes rajah* and many orchids. Veitch, greedy for more, sent out Charles Curtis and David Burke. Curtis sought and found another pitcher plant – *Nepenthes northiana* – previously known only through a painting by Marianne North. A subsequent trip to Sumatra, Java, the Moluccas as well as Borneo was rewarded with the slipper orchid, *Paphiopedilum superbiens*. Unfortunately, it was soon lost to cultivation, and the efforts of successive collectors failed to find it in the wilds again. Its accidental rediscovery is one of the more colourful tales in the romance of plant hunting, no doubt embellished by repeated telling. A Swedish collector sheltering in a hut in Sumatra noticed on one of its walls a drawing of a slipper orchid with the inscription 'C.C.'s contribution to the adornment of the house'. He realized this was the famous lost orchid and by diligent searching of the area and with more than a modicum of luck found it. A similar legend concerns yet another slipper orchid, *Paphiopedilum fairrieanum*, discovered in the Himalayas, introduced in 1857, and published in the *Botanical Magazine* the same year (plate 5024). It was admired at one of the Royal Horticultural Society's shows but suffered the same fate as *P. superbiens* by not surviving. An intensive search of the forests in North India and a reward of £1,000 met with no success. Some surveyors found it quite by chance on the borders of Bhutan in 1904.

When *Hortus Veitchii* was published in 1906 the Veitch nurseries had introduced over 200 species and varieties of orchids to British glasshouses. Veitch, Bull and Sander were the giants among orchid growers during the latter years of Victoria's reign. William Bull of King's Road, Chelsea had collectors in Colombia and his annual orchid shows, where he displayed his latest introductions and hybrids, were a spectacular sight. In 1878 he announced the arrival of 'two of the largest consignments of orchids that have ever been made. The number is estimated at 2,000,000'.

Henry F. C. Sander concentrated on orchids and, in his heyday, had no equal. Sander had served his apprenticeship in a London nursery at Forest Hill where he met a fellow German, Benedict Roezl. He employed Roezl as an orchid collector and his diligence and complete indifference to his own safety and comfort soon filled Sander's warehouses at St Albans in Hertfordshire. These

ROYAL EXOTIC NURSERY.

Kings Road, Chelsea, S.W.

April 27 1870

Dear D.r Hooker

I send down a plant of Cymbidium Canaliculatum which is I believe blooming for the first time in England. My Brother John brought it from Cape York - North Australia & although not beautiful to our idea it is so distinct that I thought

you might like to figure it.

I am dear D.r Hooker
yours sincerely
Harry Veitch

Leaves 10 — 13 ins long 1 in broad coriaceous

Bracts small 1½ times appressed to pedicels

Seps oblong obtuse Petals similar leaves as large rather obtuse

(2 fls. preserved in spirits.)

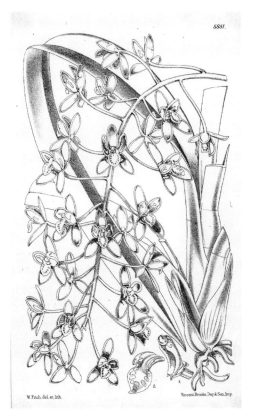

5851.

W. Fitch, del. et lith.   Vincent, Brooks, Day & Son, Imp.

Above: Letter from Sir Harry Veitch
offering *Cymbidium canaliculatum*,
collected by his brother John,
for figuring in the *Botanical Magazine*.
Left: *Cymbidium canaliculatum*
plate 5851). W. H. Fitch.

were the boom years for the orchid trade: some plants fetched more than £500 each in the sale rooms. At one time Sander had 23 collectors in the field but Roezl was always his star performer, despatching orchids by the ton. Trees were ruthlessly felled just to reach the epiphytic orchids at the top. Sites were deliberately destroyed to increase the rarity and value of the plants already collected. The Director of the Zurich Botanical Garden denounced the devastation some of these collectors wreaked. 'Not satisfied with taking 300 or 500 specimens of a fine orchid, they must scour the whole country and leave nothing for many miles around – the environs of Quito and Cuenca have been perfectly plundered and no collectors henceforth will find any Odontoglossums there. These modern collectors spare nothing. This is no longer collecting: it is wanton robbery and I wonder that public opinion is not stronger against it'.

The fever and the folly of orchidomania eventually abated: glasshouses were expensive to maintain and the whims of fashion had turned to the floral novelties of China. A fitting memorial to the orchid craze is *Reichenbachia*, the last great orchid book of the century, named after Heinrich Reichenbach, the distinguished German orchidologist. It was conceived and financed by Sander who had a lithographic printing press specially installed, and furnished a studio for the artist, H. G. Moon. He is said to have spent £7,000 on the project from which emerged four folio volumes during 1888 to 1894.

It is, however, to the volumes of the *Botanical Magazine* that the student and the scholar must turn for a continuous story of the gradual rise, the peak and the decline of orchid culture in Great Britain. The Magazine had reached its fourth volume before the first orchid – *Calopogon pulchellum* – was published in 1790. The next, *Cypripedium acaule*, was included not 'so much on account of its beauty as of its rarity' (plate 192). Only eight plates out of the first thousand depicted epiphytes. During the editorship of William Curtis and John Sims a mere 27 orchids were selected. In the first volume Sir William Hooker edited there were 11 and in 1837 – Bateman's *annus mirabilis* – the total shot up to 19. In 1849 Sir William Hooker chose 100 orchids from the Magazine, most worthy of cultivation, and Lovell Reeve published them as *A century of orchidaceous plants* (1849) on large paper to avoid the necessity of folding Fitch's plates. Thomas Moore, emulating Hooker, took 100 plates from the *Botanical Register* and Sweet's *British Flower Garden* to produce *Illustrations of orchidaceous plants* (1857). Intoxicated as he undoubtedly was by the more exotic blooms, Sir William could still find room for a rare British orchid, *Epipogium aphyllum*, proudly claiming it to be 'the first figure of it published in this country' (plate 4821).

The first volume edited by Sir Joseph Hooker in 1865 had a bumper harvest of 21 orchids, mostly described by James Bateman who continued to write the text for them for the next couple of years. He edited *A second century of orchidaceous plants*, published by Reeve in 1867.

There was a modest fall in the quantity of orchids illustrated during the last two decades of the century and Sir Trevor Lawrence, in his address to the first Orchid Conference in 1885, possibly had grounds to comment: 'I have occasionally, as a subscriber to that periodical [i.e. *Botanical Magazine*], felt a

PLATE 30
Tecomanthe speciosa. Margaret Stones. Watercolour. (*Curtis's Botanical Magazine,*
vol. 179, 1972, N.S. plate 618). The only member of Bignoniaceae native to New
Zealand survives precariously on Great Island (see page 193).

little disposed to complain that we do not yet get a few more Orchids in it'.[4] Vols. 114, 116–18, 122 and 123, in which the number of orchid plates never fell below 13, must surely have pleased him. In vol. 130 (1904), the last to be edited by Sir Joseph Hooker, the figure reaches 14, a final gesture, perhaps, of his love for this particular family of plants.

The *Botanical Magazine* has never relinquished its traditional interest in orchids. In 1981 a selection of 31 plates from the Magazine since its ownership by the Bentham-Moxon Trust was published.[5] A much more ambitious project published in 1986 includes all the orchid plates in the Magazine from its inception to 1948.[6]

In 1900 the *Botanical Magazine* made a perceptive prophesy that 'New Guinea will probably prove to be the most productive of those hitherto unexplored areas of the globe which abound in Orchids' (plate 7724). Exploration of New Guinea by the botanists Rudolf Schlechter and J. J. Smith between 1908 and 1935 disclosed over 2,000 new species, making the territory one of the richest orchid floras anywhere in the world. A recent Royal Society expedition to the Solomon Islands trebled the known population of orchids there and new species are still coming out of Borneo and the Philippines. Perhaps a mini orchid boom is under way and, therefore, enthusiasts should remember Frank Kingdon Ward's reaction to them: 'they lack all grace, they have no vitality, rarely have they even fragrance. There is something altogether sinister, a cold and ruthless hate about them'.[7] Yet even he was not entirely impervious to their charm: 'to have seen masses of gaily coloured orchids high up on some giant tropic tree is to have seen a wonderful sight'.

[4] *Journal of Royal Horticultural Society*, vol. 7(1), 1885, pp. 14–15.
[5] D. R. Hunt (ed.), *Orchids from Curtis's Botanical Magazine*, 1981.
[6] S. Sprunger, *Orchids from Curtis's Botanical Magazine*, 1986.
[7] F. Kingdon Ward, *Romance of plant hunting*, 1924.

⤳ 10 ⤵

THE LAST YEARS OF LOVELL
REEVE AND COMPANY

WHEN Soper knew of Sir Joseph Hooker's resignation, he offered the editorship of the Magazine to Kew's Director, Sir William Thiselton-Dyer. The salary was to be six guineas a month – 'the utmost the present circulation will permit' – rising to seven guineas if the circulation reached 300 and eight guineas should it top 350. While Soper did not anticipate any major changes, he thought the horticultural content could be stressed, an opinion with which Sir William concurred when he accepted the invitation. He had succeeded Sir Joseph as Director in 1885 and resented his anomalous relationship with the *Botanical Magazine*. 'The position of the Magazine as regards Kew has for some years past been not at all satisfactory. While we have been expected to supply the material for filling it and the information regarding the plants figured, I as Director have had no say in the matter . . . . It is I think obvious to you, as it is to me, that the Magazine being virtually a Kew publication should be in the hands of the Director for the time being. I therefore am prepared to undertake the editorship on the terms you offer as long as I hold that position. But you will kindly distinctly understand that I do not any way undertake to do so after I leave it'.[1]

The first issue of the Fourth Series appeared in January 1905 with six plates drawn by Matilda Smith; the price was still 3s.6d. coloured or 2s.6d. plain. Sir William dedicated the annual volume to 'my wife Harriet, Lady Thiselton-Dyer, whose grandfather and father have successively edited the "Botanical Magazine" for three quarters of a century and whose skilful pencil has contributed to its many illustrations'. Within a few months Sir William was complaining about the quality of the hand-colouring of the plates. Soper did not conceal his irritation. 'It should be borne in mind that these plates have to be drawn, printed, coloured & issued with descriptive letterpress at less than sixpence each. We will defy anyone to produce better plates at the price. Print-colourers are not artists & cannot do artists' work nor will the price permit artists' pay. All we can hope or profess to do is to give such a portrait of the plant as will give a fairly accurate idea of its structure & habit. We may add that we have not received a single complaint from any quarter except yourself'.[2] Never a man to concede an argument or give up a fight, Sir William continued to criticize the plates. Soper, his former resilience now drained by old age, was

[1] Royal Botanic Gardens, Kew. Library (Archives). English Letters 1901–05, item 1452–53, October 15, 1904.
[2] *Ibid*, Item 1458–59, April 8, 1905.

resigned to abandoning the *Botanical Magazine*. 'We are fully aware that it is in our interests to have the plates coloured as well as possible; it is an impossibility to get the plates done exactly like the coloured patterns. Unless you are willing to continue the editorship under the same conditions as before, relying upon us to get the plates done as well as we are able, we see no other way but to discontinue the Magazine at the end of the present volume'.[3] No letters survive to indicate whether this acrimonious exchange continued. In any case Sir William was deeply involved in a much more serious matter. In 1903 he had dismissed two gardeners, one of them William Purdom (the future plant collector), for enlisting the aid of two Labour Members of Parliament in their struggle to obtain better working conditions for the junior gardeners. Sir William was instructed by the Board of Agriculture to re-instate them; he resigned from the Directorship and, true to his word, from the editorship of the *Botanical Magazine* on the completion of the volume. One of his staff described him as 'a very exalted and unapproachable person, very efficient but out of sympathy with his subordinates', who 'acted as though he was the owner of the place rather than its custodian'.

The two volumes Sir William edited gave him no opportunity to impress his personality on the Magazine. He continued Botting Hemsley's practice of using the expertise of his staff for contributions; R. A. Rolfe was an obvious choice for orchids and N. E. Brown for South African plants. Sir William wrote only one description himself. The Rev. Henry Ellacombe who had made his vicarage garden at Bitton a place of pilgrimage for plant lovers, suggested to Sir William that a member of his staff should cull the pages of the *Botanical Magazine*, *Botanical Register*, etc. to compile a list of those plants which had disappeared from cultivation but nothing came of it. Botting Hemsley indexed all the plants in the first three series and prefaced it with the first comprehensive history of the Magazine based upon articles he had written in the *Gardeners' Chronicle* in 1887.[4] These two volumes are notable for at least three outstanding plants: *Nepenthes rajah*, *Meconopsis integrifolia* and *Lilium regale*.

Hugh Low discovered the giant pitcher plant, *Nepenthes rajah* (plate 8017), on Mount Kinabalu in Borneo in 1851. Its full-bellied pitcher, a deep blood-red with patches of green to attract unsuspecting insects, can hold up to two litres of liquid in which to drown its victims. F. W. Burbidge who found it again introduced it into cultivation but it is never an easy plant to grow. Sir Frederick Moore of the Botanical Garden at Glasnevin informed the *Botanical Magazine* that 'the secret of growing it seems to me to be moisture, shade and intermediate temperature. The leaves quickly get discoloured and sick when exposed to the sun'.

The meconopsis and lily were brought back by E. H. Wilson. The Veitch nursery sent him to China in 1899 to collect seed of *Davidia involucrata* with strict orders to 'stick to the one thing you are after, and do not spend time and money

[3] Royal Botanic Gardens, Kew. Library (Archives). Item 1462, September 20, 1905.
[4] W. Botting Hemsley, *A new and complete index to the Botanical Magazine from its commencement in 1787 to the end of 1904 . . . to which is prefixed a history of the Magazine*, Lovell Reeve & Co, 1906.

PLATE 31
Crocus baytopiorum. Mary Grierson. Watercolour. (*Curtis's Botanical Magazine,*
vol. 180, 1974, N.S. plate 664). A recent discovery in Turkey.

Left: *Meconopsis integrifolia* (plate 8027). Matilda Smith.
Right: *Lilium regale* (plate 8012). Matilda Smith.
Lithographed by J. N. Fitch. Collected by E. H. Wilson.

wandering about. Probably almost every worthwhile plant in China has now been introduced to Europe'. He found his *Davidia* and much else besides proving no doubt to the embarrassment of Veitch the error of their pessimistic forecast. Eleven of the 19 Chinese plants described in Thiselton-Dyer's two volumes are Wilson introductions. His name was destined to become very familiar to readers of the *Botanical Magazine*.

His second expedition for Veitch in 1903 again had a specific objective: the yellow poppywort, *Meconopsis integrifolia* (plate 8027), introduced to Europe by the French missionary, P. G. Farges, but no seed had set. Wilson found it 'in millions' at over 12,000 feet in the mountainous regions of the Chinese–Tibetan border. His greatest find on this trip and one of which he was always proud was the white trumpet *Lilium regale* – 'in adding it to Western gardens the discoverer would proudly rest his reputation with the Regal Lily', he wrote. In presenting it to its readers the *Botanical Magazine* noted that 'thirty two lilies are now recorded from China' (plate 8072). The first Chinese lily to make a comparable impact was the tiger lily, *Lilium lancifolium*, sent from Canton in 1804 by William Kerr. *Lilium regale*, being handsome and easy to grow, quickly became a garden favourite. It had been grown by the Chinese, Japanese and Koreans for over 1,000 years, making it very likely the oldest lily in cultivation. Wilson saw it in a semi-arid valley of the Min River in Sichuan. 'Not in twos or threes, but in hundreds, in thousands, aye, in tens of thousands. Its slender stems, each from two to four feet tall, flexible and tense as steel, overtopping the coarse grass and scrub and crowned with one to several large funnel-shaped flowers more or less wine-coloured without, pure white and lustrous on the face, clear canary-yellow within the tube and each stamen filament tipped with a golden anther. The air in the cool of the morning and in the evening is laden with a delicious perfume exhaled from each bloom.'[5] In 1904 Wilson shipped 300 bulbs to Veitch and in 1910, 6–7,000 to the Arnold Arboretum in the United States.

'That immense reservoir of hardy plants' is how Frank Kingdon Ward described the contorted mass of valleys, plateaus and peaks of the Himalayas stretching eastwards from Sikkim, through Assam, southern Tibet, northern Burma to meet the Chinese provinces of Yunnan, Sikang and Sichuan – more than 906,500 sq km (350,000 sq mi) of hill jungle, temperate rain forest, conifer belts, scrubland and alpine meadows. Above 2,440 m (8,000 ft), tree rhododendrons and, higher still, much smaller species flourish. In the cool moisture of forests, shrouded in mist, everything grows. In his old age Sir Joseph Hooker nostalgically remembered the alien world of virgin forests. 'I was skirting the edge of the magnificent forest that then clothed the base of the Sikkim Himalaya (now, I believe, replaced by tea plantations); twilight had just commenced, and I had scarcely realized the scene, when the Cicadas burst into full cry (it is impossible to call it song) with startling effect, sound and scene combining to herald my advance into, to me, a new world of interest and botanical excitement' (plate 7282). Travellers and naturalists explored Sikkim, Bhutan, Burma and made cautious excursions into Tibet, but at the beginning of the present century China was still largely unknown and no European had ever picked a flower in some of the remoter provinces. Up to the middle of the nineteenth century it was mainly the garden flora of China – azaleas, camellias, chrysanthemums, peonies and such-like – that was known in the West. With the exception of North America, no other part of the world has influenced British horticultural taste as much as China. It gave impetus to the Robinsonian movement of wild and woodland gardens through the apparently inexhaustible discoveries of Wilson, Forrest, Farrer, Purdom and Kingdon Ward – new gentians, lilies, meconopsis, primulas and, above all, rhododendrons. If the nineteenth century was the age of the orchid, it could be argued that the first half of the twentieth century belonged to the rhododendron.

The next editor of the *Botanical Magazine*, Sir David Prain, was acquainted with the flora of the tropics at first hand. After joining the Indian Medical Service in 1884, he became Curator of the Herbarium and Library at the Royal Botanical Garden, Calcutta three years later. In 1898 he succeeded Sir George King as Superintendent of the Garden and as Director of the Botanical Survey of India. His floristic studies in India and his botanical excursions as far north as Tibet earned him Sir Joseph Hooker's appreciative Magazine dedication in 1900. With his direct experience of Kew's imperial role, he was an eminently suitable candidate for the post of Director at Kew upon Sir William Thiselton-Dyer's resignation.

The contributors to the Magazine were no longer confined to the botanists in the Herbarium; the Curator, William Watson, and one of the senior horticultural assistants, W. J. Bean, provided cultivation notes. The innovation, however, lasted only until 1909 when the Director wrote all the descriptions but

---

[5] E. H. Wilson, *The lilies of Eastern Asia*, 1925.

Limestone cliffs in Hsing-shan, Hupeh in China. Home of *Corydalis wilsonii.*
Photograph taken by E. H. Wilson during his 1910–11 expedition.

without any of the flair or imagination of the Hookers. The hand-colouring was deteriorating too. F. L. Soper died and the business was managed by one of his sons, A. L. Soper who was, understandably, reluctant to carry on. A merger with one of the publishing houses was mooted. A meeting about the Magazine that Soper had with Arthur Hill, the Assistant Director at Kew, in October 1913 concentrated on the plates: hand-colouring, alternative methods of reproduction, the crudity of Matilda Smith's paintings, and the custody of the original drawings. This preliminary discussion was followed by a meeting with Prain a fortnight later when there was a very frank exchange of views. Soper insisted that good hand-coloured plates were superior to mechanical process work. Prain confided that Matilda Smith was incapable of heeding any opinions contrary to

PLATE 32
Echinops ruthenicus. Margaret Stones. Watercolour. (*Curtis's Botanical Magazine*,
vol. 180, 1974, N.S. plate 677). This hardy perennial is distributed throughout
South East Europe and southern U.S.S.R. to western China.

her own. As the Magazine had become so much a part of Kew's activities, Soper believed that at some time it must be officially adopted.

The publisher was still willing to complete sets of the earlier series for new subscribers. Loose plates from the Third Series could be purchased; some together with their text had been paper-wrapped into monographs on selected genera. The feasibility of the Bentham Trustees at Kew buying the back stock of the Magazine was discussed and quietly dropped. After 1915 most issues had only four plates to avoid an increase in subscription rates. In 1916, due to a shortage of staff occasioned by the War, the Magazine changed from a monthly to a quarterly.

Prain and the Keeper of the Kew Herbarium, Otto Stapf, whom he had consulted, rejected Soper's suggestion of an entire issue on *Echium* which they considered not sufficiently interesting in its structure; furthermore, they believed that 'subscribers like the feature of variety in its contents.' Soper was desperately exploring all expedients to offset the cancellation or suspension of subscriptions brought about by the war. In October 1920 he proposed both a reduction in the size and an increase in the annual subscription, and he gave notice that from 1921 he would exercise the right to retain or dispose of the original drawings as he saw fit. Sir David Prain's sharp rejoinder was that any dispute about the ownership of the drawings could jeopardize the relationship between the Magazine and Kew. He reminded Soper that it would be difficult to conduct the Magazine without access to the living collections in the Gardens and to the Herbarium and Library. Soper apologized, withdrew this contentious proposal, but resolved to terminate the Fourth Series with the current year. During the ensuing correspondence he offered the copyright and goodwill of the *Botanical Magazine* to Kew for £250. Despite its uneconomical circulation – only 400 copies of the plates and 375 copies of the letterpress were printed – Sir David Prain was, nevertheless, attracted by the proposition which he submitted to his parent body, the Ministry of Agriculture and Fisheries. While these negotiations were under way, the October/December issue of vol. 146 notified subscribers of the cessation of the Fourth Series. At the same time Lovell Reeve and Company sought to ascertain 'whether the work fulfils a sufficiently botanical and horticultural purpose to justify its continuance, and, if so, under what conditions it may be possible to do so'.

In presenting Soper's proposal to the Ministry, Sir David confidently predicted that H.M. Stationery Office with its superior organisation would soon turn a deficit into a profit. The response of the Ministry's senior officials was remarkably sympathetic. They requested H.M. Stationery Office to consider its feasibility. 'The Ministry is strongly of the opinion that in the interests of Botanical Science the publication of the Magazine in question should not be allowed to terminate'.[6] With the Magazine running at a loss, H.M. Stationery Office was not prepared to recommend its purchase. 'Under Sir David Prain's editorship it is probable that a new and independent publication would quickly succeed to the position occupied by "Curtis's Magazine" if the latter ceased

[6] Royal Botanic Gardens, Kew. Library (Archives). Bentham–Moxon files, December 30, 1920.

publication, and the goodwill is practically an incomplete list of subscribers and a deficit'.[7]

In the meanwhile the uncertain future of the *Botanical Magazine* rallied some of its loyal supporters who offered to purchase the copyright and present it to Kew provided its production was withdrawn from Lovell Reeve and Company. Sir David was cross-examined by Henry Elwes, Gerald Loder and Lionel de Rothschild at a dinner in December 1920. Rothschild spontaneously offered £100 towards buying out Lovell Reeve and Company. Elwes was more cautious and circumspect; he wanted to know whether Prain would accept the gift and conduct the Magazine as an official publication. Sir David was in favour of acceptance but could not act without his Ministry's sanction which he now sought. 'The men who have made the suggestion . . . look at it from the standpoint of representatives of families noted for several generations as patrons of gardening and of botany, who have inherited complete series of Curtis's Botanical Magazine from its foundation and who are therefore susceptible to a certain degree of sentiment with which, as an individual, and in contrast with my feelings as an officer of Government, I confess I am still able faintly to sympathize'.[8] The Ministry instructed Sir David to liaise officially in his friends' efforts to obtain the copyright and informed Soper that Kew could not purchase it.

Henry J. Elwes, whose powerful physique, confident manner and deep resonant voice commanded attention and dominated any meeting, was the principal protagonist in the negotiations that took place in 1921. F. R. S. Balfour who knew him well, said 'he had little knowledge of the arts of compromise or how to agree with his adversary in the way'. He was never easily deflected from his purpose; once when Tibetan border officials barred his entry to their country, he defiantly slipped in by an unguarded pass. In his travels in North and Central America, the Middle East and Asia, he combined sport with natural history. Sir Joseph Hooker's *Himalayan journals* had fired him with an ambition to visit India. He filled the garden of the family home at Colesborne in Gloucestershire with the plants he had collected on his travels and generously gave seeds and cuttings to other growers. Kew received his first gift of plants in 1872 and five years later Sir Joseph Hooker dedicated a volume of the *Botanical Magazine* to him. The Magazine for which he had a genuine regard, figured 96 of his plants, of which 39 he had collected himself.[9]

Elwes was not wholly in favour of handing over the Magazine to the Government. He preferred that the transfer should be to the Bentham Trust which had been founded out of the residue of the estate of the botanist, George Bentham, for the use and benefit of Kew. This was declined by the Trustees. Tentative overtures were made to the Clarendon Press at Oxford, the publishers of the *Index Kewensis*. Elwes had several meetings with Daniel Hall, the Ministry of Agriculture's Chief Scientific Adviser, about the possibility of the Magazine becoming an official publication. In anticipation of a favourable response from

[7] *Ibid*, January 31, 1921.
[8] *Ibid*, February 4, 1921.
[9] *Journal of the Royal Horticultural Society*, vol. 49, 1924, pp. 44–46.

Treasury, Hall added £500 to the Financial Estimates for its production. In May Sir David Prain received a discreet enquiry from the Smithsonian Institute in Washington hinting that it might be interested in acquiring the *Botanical Magazine*. When members at a dinner of the newly formed Garden Society on May 24 learnt from Sir David that there was some danger of the copyright going to America, Elwes and W. R. Dykes, Secretary of the Royal Horticultural Society, were instructed to obtain it on behalf of the Society. Elwes, Rothschild and Cory purchased the copyright between them and contributions were solicited from members. Elwes, Rothschild and Professor Bretland Farmer were nominated as Trustees to negotiate with the Ministry of Agriculture and H.M. Stationery Office. Everything seemed set for the *Botanical Magazine* to be published by H.M. Stationery Office under the supervision of the Ministry as a publication of Kew Gardens. The Trustees, however, wanted a legally-binding assurance that they could resume the copyright should the character, standard and number of illustrations not be maintained. As H.M. Stationery Office were not prepared to give that undertaking, thereupon the copyright was offered to, and accepted by, the Royal Horticultural Society. The Society also acquired Lovell Reeve's old stock (686 bundles of plain plates and letterpress, 39,000 coloured plates and patterns and 170 volumes). Dykes was very optimistic about the Society's ability to increase sales.

Sir David Prain, the last editor to work for the firm of Lovell Reeve, conducted the Magazine very much according to the precepts of his predecessors. But on six occasions he broke with tradition by including hybrids. Few botanical gardens and nurseries submitted plants for figuring. Private owners were not much more generous. There were exceptions, of course, like Elwes at Colesborne, T. A. Dorrien-Smith at Tresco Abbey and Canon Ellacombe at Bitton. Ellacombe gave plants in the expectation of favours in return. 'The new number of the *Botanical Magazine* wakens up my covetousness', he confessed to Sir David. 'Can you spare me *Cocculus trilobus*. It looks as if it would suit Bitton well – and are *Rosa sertata* and *R. omeiensis* in a state to be asked for? I should like both or either. The garden is full of beauty. When can you come and see it? I had Elwes here yesterday and Lynch last week'.[10] He sent Kew *Zanthoxylum planispinum* (plate 8754) only a few months before his death in 1916.

When Sir David Prain became editor in 1907, E. H. Wilson had already completed two very profitable missions to China for Veitch. Gardeners were reminded of the debt they owed to a much earlier collector, Robert Fortune, when the Magazine illustrated his honeysuckle, *Lonicera fragrantissima* (plate 8585), in 1914. Chinese plants now swamped the Magazine; Sir David approved 200 of them before he retired as editor in 1920. Three spiraeas collected by Wilson appropriately commemorated the three men who played leading roles in the discovery and introduction of Chinese plants: *S. henryi* (plate 8270), *S. veitchii* (plate 8383) and *S. wilsonii* (plate 8399). The drawing of *Primula giraldiana* (plate 8168) in 1907 announced a new collector, George Forrest. Forrest was working for the proprietor of the Cheshire nursery of Bees Limited, A. K. Bulley, whom Augustine Henry described as 'a bit of a Fabian, who wants to introduce

[10] A. Hill, *H. N. Ellacombe*, 1919, p. 191.

[166]

PLATE 33
Maurandya barclaiana. Ann Farrer. Watercolour. (*Curtis's Botanical Magazine*, vol.
183, 1981, N.S. plate 810). Although this well-known garden plant was
illustrated during the last century by the *Botanical Register* and the *Botanical
Cabinet*, it was not figured in the *Botanical Magazine* until 1981.

Ernest Henry Wilson (1876–1930).

beautiful plants to the cottages of the poor'. Most of Forrest's subsequent visits to Yunnan and South East Tibet were financed by syndicates for whom he collected seed not by the ounce but by the pound. One of his last letters reports the staggering results of his recent labours. 'Of seed, such an abundance that I scarce know where to commence. Nearly everything I wished for, and that means a lot. Primulas in profusion, seed of some of them as much as 3 to 5 lbs; some of Meconopsis, Nomocharis, Lilium, as well as bulbs of the latter. When all are dealt with and packed I expect to have nearly, if not more than, two mule loads of good clean seed, representing some 400 to 500 species, and a mule load means 130 to 150 lbs. That is something like 300 lbs of seed.' Primulas competed with rhododendrons for Forrest's attention. He introduced more than 50 species to British gardens including the dainty *Primula malacoides*.

Reginald Farrer deliberately rejected the floristically rich regions of Yunnan and Sichuan for the bleak valleys and mountains of Gansu in northwestern China. The reason for this perverse self-denial was Farrer's belief that 'with the ground so far up in the north . . . surely all plants from there must reasonably be expected to prove hardy in England – a very important point to a gardener remembering the soft and tender constitution that have given us so much disappointment in so many lovely things from the warm southerly latitudes of Yunnan and Szechuan'. With William Purdom as his companion, he found plants whose successful cultivation in Britain proved his point: *Viburnum farreri* (plate 8887), *Gentiana farreri* (plates 8874–75), *Rosa elegantula* cv. *Persetosa* (plate 8877), *Anemone tomentosa* and *Buddleja alternifolia* (plate 9085).

The last of the great collectors to establish his reputation by the outbreak of the First World War was Frank Kingdon Ward, originally engaged by A. K. Bulley but, like Forrest, later to work for syndicates. Forrest was a diffident speaker and a reluctant author but Kingdon Ward's fresh and incisive style makes all his books eminently readable. In this passage he evokes a scene high up in the mountains, the dark smudge of forest far below, and the sound of tinkling water from melting snow filling the clear air. 'Everywhere are miniature rhododendrons as creeping plants plastered against the rocks or as heather – like tuflets or stunted bushes crouching in the stony hollows in an indescribable rainbow of colour. Splashes of blood-red, shell-pink, yellow, purple and mauve break upon the eye as it roves round the scene'.

The bond that linked all these collectors was a love of rhododendrons, the plant that ranges from tall trees to prostrate shrublets, from demure to flamboyant flowers in a bewitching spectrum of both subtle and strident colours. After Robert Fortune collected *Rhododendron fortunei* in the mountains of Ning Po in 1855, Sir Joseph Hooker forecast that 'the centre of the Rhododendron area is certainly Eastern Asia, from both the tropical and temperate regions of which continent new species are constantly turning up' (plate 5596). That was in 1866; in 1890 after the discoveries of Delavay and Henry, he had even more reason to repeat the same confident prediction. 'Judging by the results of botanical explorations lately made in Western China, it would appear that all previous estimates of the number of species of this magnificent genus of plants, are far below the mark, and that the discoveries made in the Eastern Himalaya are only harbingers of what are to be expected from the vast mountain regions still further to the east' (plate 7149). By 1908 E. H. Wilson had collected 70 Chinese species, and succeeded in introducing about 50. Between 1910 and 1920 the efforts of Wilson, Forrest, Farrer and Kingdon Ward added no fewer than 312 new species.

Outstripping all of them was George Forrest with 260 new species to his credit, a contribution recognized as 'immortal, something more lasting than bronze'. In a letter of 1917 he discloses that 'in going over my fieldbook I find Rhododendron comprises some 15 per cent. of the total, and over a certain altitude in N.W. Yunnan Rhododendrons dominate the flora. They are so numerous in species and varieties that I now find myself in a perfect tangle over them, and have given up even attempting to group them in the field'.[11] Fortunately, he could leave this taxonomic nightmare to the world's leading authority on the flora of western China, and in particular rhododendrons and primulas, Sir Isaac Bayley Balfour. At the Edinburgh Botanic Garden where he was Director, Balfour and his assistants formulated a tentative classification of the exploding population of species into a number of series and sub-series.

The *Botanical Magazine* conscientiously reported the prevailing botanical and horticultural interest in the genus; 138 of the 1,700 plates between 1905 and 1948 depicted rhododendrons. Any species of exceptional quality was drawn by the Magazine's artists; in 1938 it was *R. vernicosum* (plates 8904–05), collected by both Wilson and Forrest; in 1940 *R. taggianum* (plate 9612), 'the gem of Forrest's 1925 collection'; in 1972 *R. concatenans* (N.S. plate 634), dubbed 'Orange Bill' by Kingdon Ward. When China became inaccessible after the Communist revolution, botanists and collectors turned to relatively unexplored regions like New Guinea. *R. macgregoriae* (N.S. plate 552) was one of the first of the new species from that island to be published in the Magazine. *R. wrightianum* (N.S. plate 653), *R. zoelleri* (N.S. plate 682) and *R. auvigeranum* (N.S. plate 787) were a few more random pickings from nearly 300 species collected there.

New Guinea rhododendrons can only be grown in temperate greenhouses but many of those from the Sino-Himalayas are hardy on acid soil in Britain.

[11] J. G. Millais, *Rhododendrons*, Second Series, 1924, p. 17.

PLATE 34
Paphiopedilum tonsum. Pandora Sellars. Watercolour. (*Curtis's Botanical Magazine,*
vol. 184, 1982, N.S. plate 838). This orchid was collected by Charles Curtis in
the East Indies in 1882 for the Veitch nursery at Chelsea.

Rhododendron woods became a familiar pattern in the landscape and some growers made them a spectacular feature: J. C. Williams at Caerhays Castle, the Marquess of Headfort at Kells, Lionel de Rothschild at Exbury, Stephenson R. Clarke at Borde Hill, E. J. P. Magor at Lamellen and J. B. Stevenson at Tower Court. In 1875 Shirley Hibberd protested that 'the money spent on rhododendrons during twenty years in this country would nearly suffice to pay off the National Debt'.[12] One wonders what his reaction would have been to their astonishing popularity some 50 years later. Some years ago when a letter in *The Times* provocatively advocated a 'Kill a rhododendron a day' campaign, it provoked protests from earnest enthusiasts.

Rhododendrons were at home in the mild moist climate of Cornwall at Caerhays Castle where John Charles Williams started growing them about 1885. He was a loyal patron of Wilson and Forrest. Several of Wilson's rhododendrons were first flowered at Caerhays: *R. fargesii*, *R. sutchuense* and *R. auriculatum*. The red-carmine blooms of *R. orbiculare* were a particular favourite with Williams. 'I think I would prefer to keep a good plant of it if I were only to be allowed one of the whole family', he told Prain. 'Wilson told me he found it with his glasses on the far side of a deep valley [in Sichuan] and that it took him a day and a half's journey to get there' (plate 8775). He sent Forrest's seed to Kew and 15 of his rhododendrons were drawn for the Magazine. The Marquess of Headfort was also a recipient of Forrest's bounty. On his estate at Kells in County Meath rhododendrons from India, Burma, China and Tibet vied with conifers (which earned him the Veitch Memorial Medal), rare shrubs and deciduous trees. During the term of office of three editors of the *Botanical Magazine* – O. Stapf, Sir Arthur Hill and W. B. Turrill – 87 plates were derived from plants grown at Kells, 19 of them rhododendrons.

Like orchids, rhododendrons were subjected to the hybridists' skill. Hooker's Indian rhododendrons and Fortune's *R. fortunei* were parents of a fertile family. J. C. Williams made about 20 or 30 crosses a year; Lionel de Rothschild successfully nurtured hybrids that incorporated the desirable attributes of hardiness and size of flower; Lord Aberconway made Bodnant celebrated for rhododendron varieties with good foliage and rich colouring. This enthusiasm led to the formation of the Rhododendron Society in 1915 which held its first exhibition in 1926 and published *The species of Rhododendron* in 1930.

---

[12] S. Hibberd, *The amateur's flower garden*, 1875, p. 216.

~ 11 ~

THE PURSUIT OF PLANTS

PLANT hunters, professional and amateur, have diligently searched the
world for the familiar as well as the novel, the strange as well as the
spectacular. The more inhospitable the terrain, the greater the challenge
and the more rewarding the achievement. Kingdon Ward wrote with feeling of
'dense jungle, impassable rivers, snow-bound passes, incredible rain, above all
lack of roads, of transport, of food, of shelter in an almost uninhabited land'.
They were often genuine explorers, travelling through unmapped territory.
They were threatened, molested and sometimes killed by hostile natives or
xenophobic Chinese and Tibetans. Few escaped illness and disease. Linnaeus's
pupils – he preferred to call them 'apostles' – were inspired by him to explore the
flora of America, Africa and Asia and some died in the cause of botany. Linnaeus
felt a twinge of guilt. 'The deaths of many whom I have induced to travel have
made my hair grey, and what have I gained? A few dried plants, and with great
anxiety, unrest and care'.

Sometimes it was their misfortune to die on their very first expedition like
John Forbes on the Zambesi; or like the two eager young gardeners from
Chatsworth, Peter Banks and Robert Wallace, sent to North America with the
advice 'to beware of bears and women, both hindrances to the quiet life of a
plant collector', who were drowned trying to shoot the rapids on the Columbia
River.

Tropical diseases took their toll. Richard Pearce was a victim of yellow fever
in Panama; Gustav Wallis died of some unspecified fever in Ecuador; William
Griffith succumbed to malaria in Malaya; and debonair Victor Jacquemont
expired in a Bombay hospital. The climate and physical exhaustion im-
perceptibly weakened the body: pneumonia probably caused Reginald Farrer's
death in Burma, while George Forrest died of a heart attack in China. Some
were drowned at sea, or, wearied by strenuous collecting, died on the voyage like
the unfortunate William Brass returning home from Africa.

David Douglas was gored and trampled to death by a wild bull trapped in a
pit into which Douglas fell. Richard Cunningham, a clerk at Kew Gardens, who
became Colonial Botanist in New South Wales, was killed by aborigines; the
French missionary collector, Jean Soulié, was tortured and murdered by
marauding Tibetan monks; and as recently as 1919 the Canadian botanist,
Charles Robinson, fell a victim to headhunters on the lonely island of Amboina.
A few like John Jeffrey in the western United States and Frederick Müller in
Mexico disappeared without trace, never to be heard of again. It was rumoured
that William Kerr became an opium addict while he was in Canton; he died
within a few years of taking charge of a garden in Ceylon.

What were the qualities demanded of men rash enough to risk their health and even their lives for the gratification of gardeners and botanists? E. H. Wilson, the doyen of plant collectors, enumerated them succinctly. 'First and foremost it is the work of youth for it takes heavy toll of strength and endurance, patience and enthusiasm. A sound constitution and an eminently sane mind are fundamental requisites. An optimistic temperament and abundance of tact are essential in dealing with the difficulties and delays incident upon travel and the idiosyncracies of native peoples'.[1] While he was an assistant at the Royal Botanic Garden in Edinburgh, George Forrest insisted on walking the 10 km (6 mi) to and from his home and stoically disdained a chair or stool while he worked at a table in the herbarium – a habit indicative of the stamina and resolution which were to serve him well in Yunnan. Frank Kingdon Ward, terrified of heights, forced himself to climb precipitous mountain paths and to cross flimsy rope and bamboo bridges.

Collectors were, by circumstance if not by inclination, solitaries, cut off for long periods from the companionship of urban life. David Burke was one who welcomed the separation; J. H. Veitch said of him that he was 'one of those natures who live more or less with the natives as a native and apparently prefer this mode of life'. Highly successful expeditions have, of course, been made by collectors working not on their own, but as a member of a team. A bond of extraordinary harmony existed between that incongruous pair, the volatile and extravagant Farrer and the reticent and taciturn Purdom. The partnership of Ludlow and Sherriff was immensely profitable.

A plant collector needs not only a knowledge of plants and their habitats but also a discerning eye for those of potential horticultural value, an ability to assess colour, fragrance, habit and ease of cultivation. Good field notes are invaluable – George Forrest was exemplary in this respect and he turned his knowledge of geological strata and minerals to good account.

It is a matter of conjecture what qualities in Francis Masson made Sir Joseph Banks choose him as Kew's first collector. He was engaged in 1772 at an annual salary of £100 with an expenses allowance of £200. The salary was still £100 when Kew sent William Kerr to China in 1803. John Livingstone, the surgeon in Canton, thought it was 'almost too small for his necessary wants, and he consequently lost respect and consideration in the eyes even of the Chinese assistants whom he was obliged to employ'. When Robert Fortune complained of the inadequacy of this now customary £100, the Horticultural Society of London haughtily replied that 'the mere pecuniary returns of your mission ought to be but a secondary consideration to you'. Almost a century after Masson's appointment, Kew had not improved on his salary. The document appointing Richard Oldham as a Kew collector in 1861 is carefully explicit about the financial arrangements. Out of his £100 salary Oldham was to 'provide himself with clothes, etc. and defray the expenses of his mess, and all other expenses of a personal nature'[2] when on board ship or not actually

[1] E. H. Wilson, *Plant hunting*, 1927.
[2] Royal Botanic Gardens, Kew. Library (Archives). Kew collectors, vol. 9, 1861–64, Oldham.

Francis Masson (1741–1805).   Robert Fortune (1812–1880).

collecting. An additional £80–£100 was authorized for living expenses and equipment while he was in the field. Oldham was instructed to keep a meticulous record of all expenditure. 'Sir William Hooker trusts entirely to Richard Oldham's prudence, economy and judgement for the proper expenditure of this money'. Perhaps frugality should also have been added to the qualities of the ideal plant collector.

Collectors worked for individuals, botanical gardens, nurseries, societies and syndicates. Syndicates are perhaps the most demanding of employers. Only very efficient organization enabled George Forrest to fulfil the expectations of his financial backers. This terse statement in a contract engaging Forrest suggest they had little idea of the vast distances they expected him to travel. 'Mr Forrest will as soon as practicable make and conduct to Bhamo in Upper Burma and thence to the regions or distances next hereinafter mentioned an expedition for the purpose of collecting bulbs, seeds and plants of horticultural value and also botanical specimens of plants in the regions or districts situate in the western and north-western parts of the Province of Yunnan, the western parts of the Province of Szechuan (in China) and the south-eastern parts of Tibet (or such of the said regions or districts as may for the time being be accessible) and for other purposes hereinafter mentioned'.[3]

Before the Horticultural Society of London sent Robert Fortune to China in 1843, they required his assenting signature to a long document stipulating his duties and responsibilities. He was to collect seeds and plants of ornamental or economic interest. He was advised to visit one of the northern provinces where the flora was likely to be hardy in Britain. 'In all cases you will bear in mind that hardy plants are of the first importance to the Society, and that the value of the plants diminishes as the heat required to cultivate them is increased. Aquatics, Orchidaceae or plants producing very handsome flowers are the only exceptions to this rule'.[4] His shopping list included azaleas, bamboos, camellias, nepenthes, peonies, water-lilies, double yellow roses, tea, peaches, oranges and other citrus fruit. For good measure he was to look out for blue peonies, 'the existence of

[3] J. M. Cowan, *The journeys and plant introductions of George Forrest*, 1952, p. 8.
[4] *Journal of the Royal Horticultural Society*, vol. 68, 1943, p. 164.

PLATE 35

Arisaema costatum. Pandora Sellars. Watercolour. (*Kew Magazine*, vol. 1, part 2, 1984, plate 7). Their extraordinary flowers and attractive foliage have made arisaemas popular plants in temperate gardens.

which is, however, doubtful', and yellow camellias, 'if such exist'. He was to bring back samples of soil, especially that in which the best specimens of azaleas, camellias and chrysanthemums flourished. He was to discover the techniques the Chinese used for growing miniature trees, why they mixed seeds with burnt bone and how they made and used manure. Being a plant collector for the Horticultural Society extended far beyond conventional duties into a fact-finding mission. And all for a salary of £100 a year! Fortune, not very happy about having to defend himself against any aggressive Chinese with nothing more than a stick, requested fire-arms for his own protection. With some reluctance the Society provided him with a fowling piece and pistols which Fortune used to good effect on the occasion his boat was attacked by Chinese pirates.

Francis Masson travelled the great plains of the Cape Flats in the comparative comfort of a well-provisioned trek waggon, covered with a sail-cloth canopy, pulled by a team of oxen. David Douglas had a tent which he rarely used, preferring the shelter of a tree or an upturned canoe. He travelled light from choice, living off the land and consequently often desperately short of food. 'The following day found me so broken with fatigue and starvation, and my knees so much worse, that I could not stir out. We fared most scantily on the roots of *Sagittaria sagittifolia* and *Lupinus littoralis* till, crawling out a few steps with my gun I providentially saw some wild birds, and killed five ducks with one shot. To save time in plucking the fowl, I singed off the feathers, and with a basin of tea, made a good supper on one of them'. Masson usually had a companion on his trips; he joined the Swedish botanist, Carl Thunberg, on several journeys into the interior, and on short excursions Lady Anne Monson travelled with him.

Until his second marriage in 1947, when his wife went along with him, Frank Kingdon Ward travelled alone apart from a retinue of porters. George Forrest, on the other hand, had the company of a large band of native collectors. It was not unusual for collectors to train natives who knew the countryside to help them. Augustine Henry and E. H. Wilson depended upon them but it was Forrest who shaped his casual labour into an efficient team. At one time he had

Type of waggon used by F. Masson on his plant-collecting expeditions in the Cape.
(W. J. Burchell, *Travels in the interior of southern Africa*, vol. 1, 1822, p. 148).

[176]

up to 20 men harvesting plants and seeds over a wide area. So well did he train his hillmen that they could be relied upon to work on their own while he was on leave in England. There were drawbacks and dangers in this practice: choice specimens could be overlooked; the wrong material could be collected or seeds taken before they were ripe. Farrer and Kingdon Ward preferred a smaller yield and a more restricted area to explore in order to see all the plants themselves, to note their location and to return later in the year to collect their seed. Kingdon Ward was insistent on the correctness of this procedure. 'The plant collector must see his plants in flower in order to know what to take and which to leave; he must see them in fruit in order to gather seed'.

Farrer, true to his mercurial personality, quickly searched the hills but always alert. Forrest was more methodical and painstaking. He would carefully record relevant data: a description of the plant, altitude, soil, press a specimen and allocate a field number. 'From these specimens, when seed has been collected, a technical description is drawn up . . . . Also the seeds when brought in are numbered, so no mistake can arise later. These specimens serve a double purpose; when sending my men out I generally break up the party considerably, and, as all of them have not so retentive memories as myself and the chief collector, who can give me points at times, I used to take out the specimens for the day's collecting and freshen them up as to the localities of the plants'.[5] Sir Joseph Banks also required comprehensive records. 'Whenever you meet with ripe seeds of plants you are carefully to collect them', he instructed Archibald Menzies, the surgeon and naturalist on Captain Vancouver's survey of the Pacific coast of North America in 1791, 'and, having dried them properly, to put them up in paper packages, writing on the outside or in a corresponding list, such particulars relative to the soil and climate, where each was found and the mode of culture most likely to succeed with it'.

There were conflicting opinions regarding the collection of seeds in the eighteenth century. Richard Bradley at Cambridge University urged that the seeds of legumes should not be taken out of their pods nor the pulp removed from stone fruit as 'Nature has provided proper coverage for every seed to defend it from injuries'. James Lee of the Vineyard Nursery at Hammersmith believed that 'plums or peaches, will keep best divested of the pulp or outer coat'.[6] Some seeds quickly lost their viability and others, as David Douglas sadly discovered, provided convenient meals for roving rats. Seeds were easy to transport and together with bulbs and roots could be stowed away in leather pouches and saddle bags. Plants, on the other hand, posed many difficulties. Improvisation could surely go no further than the use of ox bladders as water containers into which plants, their roots lightly covered with soil, could be placed. That was the method earnestly recommended in the 1730s to John Bartram, the North American collector. Richard Spruce, bringing his precious cinchona plants from the Andes in 1859 could keep them alive only by constant watering but then, to his dismay, he discovered that 'there was a risk of their damping off . . . . In a few weeks the cuttings began to root and then they were attacked by

[5] J. M. Cowan, *The journeys and plant introductions of George Forrest*, 1952, p. 23.
[6] J. Lee, *Rules for collecting and preserving seeds from Botany Bay*, 1787.

PLATE 36

Echinocereus pectinatus var. *dasyacanthus* (upper); *Echinocereus rigidissimus* var.
rubispinus (lower). Christabel King. Watercolour. (*Kew Magazine*, vol. 1, part 4,
1984, plate 24) Echinocereus is one of the most widely cultivated genera in the
family Cactaceae.

caterpillars'. Plants which survived transportation to the coast sometimes had a chance of recuperating in gardens and nurseries before being loaded on ships. But having got them safely to a port was not always the end of the matter for the anxious collector. Ships were full or captains and crew were hostile to the prospect of tubs of plants cluttering the deck. Francis Masson, waiting patiently at the Cape for a passage for his plants was often despondent. 'I put up several considerable collections to be ready, particularly one of very curious Bulbs which I have been obliged to unpack and Plant in Pots and Boxes . . . . I have many new Succulent plants, some very curious Stapelias, Euphorbias, etc. but how I shall get them home, God only knows'.[7]

The accounts that Sir Joseph Hooker, E. H. Wilson, R. Farrer and F. Kingdon Ward have written of their adventures have become classics in travel literature. Even the laconic David Douglas displayed an unexpected narrative skill when he confided to his journal a perilous encounter with Indians. 'The huge cones (on the growing trees) were like small sugar loafs in the grocers' shop. I took my gun and was busy clipping them from the branches with ball when eight Indians came at the report of my gun. They were all painted with red earth, armed with bows and arrows, spears of bone and flint knives and appeared to me to be anything but friendly. I endeavoured to explain to them what I wanted and they seemed satisfied and sat down to smoke, but had no sooner done so than I perceived one string his bow and another sharpen his flint knife with a pair of wooden pincers and hang it on the wrist of his right hand which gave me ample testimony of their inclination. To save myself I could not do by flight and without hesitation I went backwards six paces and cocked my gun and then pulled from my belt one of my pistols which I held in my left hand. I was determined to fight for life. I as much as possible endeavoured to preserve my coolness and perhaps did so. I stood eight or ten minutes looking at them and they at me without a word passing until one at last, who seemed to be the leader, made a sign for tobacco which I said they should get on condition of going and searching me some cones. They went, and disappearing I beat a quick retreat. How irksome is such a night to me. I can't speak a word to my guides, not a book to read and constantly in expectation of attack and the position I am now lying in is lying on the grass writing by the light of my Columbia candle, namely a piece of wood containing resin'.

The reticent and uncommunicative George Forrest was persuaded to contribute an article to the *Gardeners' Chronicle* in May 1910 on 'The perils of plant collecting' in which he recounted an incident on his very first expedition to Yunnan in 1904. Tibetan monks having wiped out a Chinese garrison at a small trading station on the east bank of the Mekong were killing all the foreigners they could find. Forrest who was collecting in the neighbourhood thought it prudent to withdraw together with two aged French priests. Unfortunately, their presence was discovered and they were pursued by a band of armed Tibetans and ambushed. Over 60 of the party including the French priests were killed; only one of Forrest's 17 collectors and servants escaped. Forrest fled towards the river to find the Tibetans waiting for him. 'For a fraction of time I

[7] M. Gunn and L. E. Codd, *Botanical exploration of southern Africa*, 1981, p. 248.

Francis Kingdon Ward (1885–1958). George Forrest (1873–1932).

hesitated; being armed with a Winchester repeating rifle, 12 shots, a heavy revolver and two belts of cartridges, I could easily have made a stand, but I feared being unable to clear a passage before those whom I knew to be behind me arrived on the scene'. He escaped into the dense jungle and somehow eluded his pursuers. For more than a week he hid, subsisting on a few ears of wheat and a handful of dried peas. 'At the end of eight days I had ceased to care whether I lived or died – my feet swollen out of all shape, my hands and face torn with thorns, and my whole person coated with mire'. He made one last bid for freedom and miraculously found friendly villagers who gave him refuge, food and guides to take him over the summit of the mountain. Descending towards the Mekong he had the misfortune to step on a concealed bamboo spike which passed right through his foot. 'I suffered excruciating agony for many days, and it was months before the wound healed completely'. He eventually reached the safety of a Chinese garrison but he had lost everything: his equipment, stores and the plants and seeds of a whole season's collecting.

The peaks in a plant collector's life are those occasions when he finds a really outstanding plant or rediscovers one that has been lost. The first time that Wilson went to China to look for *Davidia involucrata* was a memorable experience for him. Long after he had left China, Augustine Henry still recalled a ride along a river valley and then suddenly seeing on the other side a solitary *Davidia* in full flower 'waving its innumerable ghost handkerchiefs'. When Henry's specimens of the tree were being drawn at Kew in 1891 for Hooker's *Icones Plantarum*, the Keeper of the Herbarium enthusiastically commented: 'Davidia is a tree almost deserving a special mission to western China with a view to its introduction to European gardens'. Wilson found the spot where Henry had seen it but all that was left of the tree was a forlorn stump; the tree had been chopped down the previous year for timber to build a house. Dismayed but not discouraged, Wilson continued to seek the elusive tree and his persistence was rewarded when on May 19, 1900 – a date he would never forget – he found a splendid specimen, 15 m (50 ft) tall, covered with blossom. His luck held for within 160 km (100 mi) he came across another ten trees. He waited anxiously for them to fruit, conscious all the time of personal danger from Boxer insurgents.

A journey to dig up bulbs of *Lilium regale* almost cost him his life. He was hit in an avalanche of rocks on a high mountain pass. He improvized splints with his camera tripod for his broken leg and was carried for three days in considerable pain to a Presbyterian Mission for medical treatment. But he got his bulbs safely to the Arnold Arboretum in Boston and his casual comment some years afterwards was 'the royal lily was worth it and more'.

For Reginald Farrer, *Gentiana farreri* more than compensated for the expense and hardship of two years on the Chinese – Tibetan frontier. He found a meadow of azure blue and walked in intoxicated delight on a mat of gentians unable to step 'anywhere on the moor without crushing at least half a dozen of its imperious trumpets'. George Forrest happened upon a mass of the double white form of *Rosa banksiae* in a valley in Yunnan, 'a hundred or more feet in length, thirty feet high and twenty through, a veritable cascade of the purest white backed by the most delicate green, and with a cushion of fragrance on every side. One sight such as that', he added, 'and it is only one of many, is worth all the weariness and hardship of a journey from England'.[8]

Such experiences are the rich and rightful reward of the plant collector with perhaps the benediction of a modest immortality, should one of his discoveries be named after him. In all his books, written in a ripe exuberance of language, Reginald Farrer communicates not only the moments of exhilaration but also a constant contentment. 'With a feeling of being at home once more, I sprawled at ease on my spring cushions of Potentilla and Honeysuckle, contemplating the vast loveliness of the world with that curious proprietary feeling that such loveliness gives – as if one somehow owned it, or were responsible for it, and had a right to be proud of it'.[9]

[8] J. M. Cowan, *The journeys and plant introductions of George Forrest*, 1952, p. 30.
[9] R. Farrer, *The rainbow bridge*, 1921, p. 221.

Panoramic view of south-east flank of the Lichiang Range, Yunnan in China.
Lush meadow with senecio, delphinium, aconitum, etc. in foreground;
marginal scrub of berberis, cotoneaster, etc.; conifer forest.
Photograph taken by G. Forrest in 1919.

THE ROYAL
HORTICULTURAL SOCIETY
AND KEW

HE Royal Horticultural Society, the new owners of the *Botanical Magazine*, had several problems to resolve: how was it going to be published, who was going to edit and illustrate it, and how was the absence of any numbers since vol. 146 in 1920 to be tackled. A Botanical Magazine Committee was formed, which after discreet enquiries, invited the scientific publishers, H. F. and G. Witherby, to tender for a contract to last three years. Acceptable terms were agreed with Witherby and it was decided to print 600 copies of the first volume – an optimistic forecast of sales as current subscriptions were well below 300; wisely only 250 were to be coloured initially.

A successor had to be found for Sir David Prain who retired as Director at Kew in 1922. Presumably Arthur Hill, the new Director, did not want the extra responsibility of editor at that particular stage of his career. Dr Otto Stapf who had just retired as Keeper of the Herbarium and Library at Kew was suggested for the post. He had been a student and assistant to Kerner von Marilaun at the University in Vienna and had written flower studies of Persia before his appointment as Assistant for India in the Kew Herbarium in 1890. He contributed to the *Flora Capensis* and *Flora of Tropical Africa* and on Botting Hemsley's retirement in 1908, followed him as Keeper. A distinguished taxonomist with a reputation for meticulous scholarship made him an admirable choice. Stapf accepted the appointment and the Magazine became an absorbing interest during his retirement.

H. J. Elwes who had played a prominent part in the purchase of the copyright obtained the services of Miss Lilian Snelling as artist to succeed Matilda Smith, now in her late sixties. In July 1920 he had sounded out Arthur Hill about the possibility of work at Kew for Miss Snelling whom he had launched in her career as a botanical artist. 'I believe from what I have seen & heard that poor old Miss Smith is not likely to be able to do justice to the Drawing much longer. I enclose a letter from Miss Snelling whose lovely flower paintings are unsurpassed if equalled by any other artist that I know, & who has been working for two years at Edinburgh under Balfour's special guidance & tuition, but as he cannot keep her on as a member of staff after October she has to look for another job as it is all she has to depend on'.[1] Living at St Mary Cray in Kent, it was considered possible for her to come to Kew two or three times a week. She was also a

[1] Royal Botanic Gardens, Kew. Library (Archives). IRHS/16.

PLATE 37
Cyclamen pseudibericum. Mary Grierson. Watercolour. (*Cyclamen*, Kew Magazine
Monograph, in preparation).

Lilian Snelling (1879–1972).

lithographer, having studied the craft under Frank Morley Fletcher. The Royal Horticultural Society had no hesitation in offering her the post. Her remuneration was to be 25s. for each drawing and another 15s. for redrawing it on zinc for reproduction and for colouring a pattern plate for the colourists. The Royal Horticultural Society decided that all the original drawings executed for the Magazine should be added to the existing collection in the Kew Herbarium in return for a continuance of Kew's facilities.

At its January meeting in 1922, the Botanical Magazine Committee agreed not to bring out a volume for 1921. At its next monthly meeting, one of its members, Reginald Cory, generously offered to finance the production of the 1921 volume. He was a coal-shipper, the owner of a fine library of illustrated botanical and horticultural books and a keen gardener. At his home at Duffryn near Cardiff he grew many of the Chinese introductions of Wilson and Forrest. His offer was gratefully accepted and plate numbers were allocated to the volume to preserve the numerical sequence of the series.

After a lapse of nearly two years, the *Botanical Magazine* resumed publication in October 1922. The vignette of the Palm House at Kew was retained on the wrapper, but the designation 'Fourth Series' was dropped and the phrase 'Private gardens' was added to the title. The price which had been kept unrealistically low by Lovell Reeve and Company was sharply increased to 17s.6d. an issue or 63s. annual subscription. Lilian Snelling made her début as artist and lithographed not only her own work but also the plates drawn by M. Smith, A. Kellet and G. Atkinson. Her drawings of Chinese plants had been done years earlier for Sir Isaac Bayley Balfour at the Edinburgh Botanic Garden which generously allowed the Magazine to use a selection of them. Nearly half of the 44 plates featured plants from China, Tibet, Japan and Burma. *Scadoxus multiflorus* ssp. *multiflorus* from the Sudan was one of the last contributions from Elwes who died in November 1922. In a graceful tribute, Stapf acknowledged the indebtedness of all gardeners to him. 'Rarely has a private garden conducted on so simple lines as that at Colesborne Park yielded so much in return for the love and skill bestowed on it' (plate 8975). In 1922 Kew purchased from a

[184]

Oenothera acaulis. Above: Some original
sketches by Lilian Snelling.
Right: Published plate (N.S. 135)
in *Botanical Magazine.*

member of the Curtis family another 165 original drawings mostly done for the
Magazine between 1830 and 1834.[2]

Even though the Magazine had an excellent editor and artist, it still failed to
break even, let alone make a profit, and the Royal Horticultural Society found
itself committed to a £500 annual subsidy. Witherby blamed the 'too scientific
and too botanical' character of the Magazine. In their opinion the Latin
diagnoses should be omitted, floral dissections on the plates should be simplified,
and horticulturists rather than botanists should be its clientèle. When
Witherby's contract expired in December 1924, an estimate from Messrs
Bernard Quaritch was accepted, and vol. 151 appeared under their imprint.

For some years Thomas Hay, Superintendent of the Central Parks in London,
had been collecting portraits of the people to whom successive volumes of the
Botanical Magazine had been dedicated since 1827 when Sir William Hooker
initiated the practice. A fellow member of the Royal Horticultural Society
Council, William Cuthbertson, encouraged their publication as a supplementary volume to the Magazine. Cuthbertson paid for the research and the Society
the printing costs.[3]

Curtis's Botanical Magazine dedications was conceived and produced in a

[2] *Kew Bulletin,* 1923, p. 176.
[3] E. Nelmes and W. Cuthbertson, *Curtis's Botanical Magazine dedications, 1827–1927* [*100*]
portraits and biographical notes, 1931.

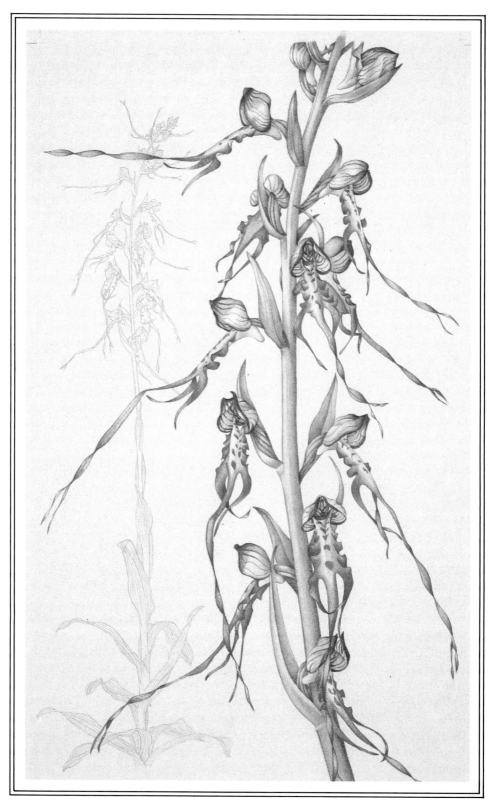

commendably short space of time. A similar promptitude unfortunately did not attend the progress of the volume that Cory had volunteered to sponsor. Although Edinburgh had lent him paintings by Lilian Snelling, all that he had done with them by 1928 was to have three of them chromolithographed as part of his research into other reproduction processes. Stapf was asked to supervise its completion and within three years he had all the plates drawn on zinc and colour patterns prepared. Much of the text was also in print when Cory decided he wanted to make alterations. In January 1933, frustrated and irritated, Stapf relinquished his editorship of the volume. With the death of Stapf in August and of Cory the following year, John Ramsbottom, Keeper of Botany at the Natural History Museum, became editor, enlisted the aid of colleagues to write the few outstanding descriptions, and got it published in 1938. Half the material for the 59 plates came from Edinburgh; Lilian Snelling drew and lithographed most of them: two – plates 8901 and 8929 – were produced by a mechanical process. All the great contemporary plant collectors were represented: Wilson, Forrest, Kingdon Ward and Cooper. There were 11 rhododendrons including *R. vernicosum*, praised as 'one of the most generally useful of all the Rhododendrons introduced to cultivation from Western China' (plates 8904–05); ten primulas from China, two from Japan and one from Tibet. A folded plate was given to *Gentiana farreri* (plate 8874–75), by then a common resident in many rock gardens. A set of the plates, coloured with especial care, on large paper was presented to both the Royal Horticultural Society and Kew.

Chinese plants also dominated the nine volumes edited by Stapf. Indeed he dedicated his first volume in 1922 to George Forrest 'as a token of our admiration of the energy, courage and sagacity with which he has in repeated expeditions since 1904 explored the flora of the borderland of Yunnan and Tibet'. He included Forrest's *Gentiana sino-ornata* (plate 9241) and another favourite, the blue poppy, *Meconopsis betonicifolia* (plate 9185), discovered by Delavay but introduced into general cultivation by Kingdon Ward. Farrer and Purdom are represented, amongst others, by *Clematis macropetala* (plate 9142). Purdom was content to note it simply as a 'handsome blue-flowered slight trailer'. Farrer, however, lyrically described it as rambling 'fraille through light bushes, to the height of two or three feet, and then cascades downwards in a fall of lovely great flowers of softest china-blue'.

As an authority on grasses, Stapf could not resist including *Spartina townsendii* (plate 9125) successfully used for stabilizing and solidifying mud in coastal defence work. Stapf's constant concern for accuracy led him to commission a new drawing of *Berberis hookeri* (plate 9153) as the original plate in 1852 showed only the fruiting state and its accompanying description had errors.

Stapf reverted to the practice of inviting members of the staff and outside authorities to contribute under their own names although he still wrote many of the descriptions himself. The latter were expanded into a scholarly investigation and resolution of complicated problems of taxonomy and nomenclature, sometimes in the process revising genera. Whenever possible he consulted type specimens in his painstaking verification of determinations. Notes on geographical distribution, ecology, origin and date of introduction and cultivation completed the regular pattern of information. His whole-hearted commitment to the *Botanical Magazine* set exacting standards for subsequent editors.

The next editor, Sir Arthur Hill, was beset with problems of hand-colouring. Lilian Snelling adapted her drawings to make it easier for colourists to apply simple washes of colour. From 1935 a better quality and whiter paper was used for the plates. But hand-colouring was now an expensive anachronism and F. R. Durham, the Secretary of the Royal Horticultural Society, said the Society could not afford this luxury for much longer. 'There seems to my mind only two alternatives facing it', he told Sir Arthur in 1937; 'one is to cut down the number of plates or to produce the Magazine half yearly with a reduced number of plates, and the other is to popularize the whole thing so that the best form of colour printing can be adopted and the Magazine made a supplement to the Journal, Fellows subscribing extra who desire to have the coloured supplement'.[4] The Society was not able to pay the colourists more and a year later he was gloomily forecasting that rising costs would bring about the demise of the Magazine. The death of Mr Jatter, the head of a family of colourists, in January 1939 precipitated the crisis he feared. It proved extremely difficult to find people prepared to undertake routine hand-colouring and, at the same time, maintain acceptable standards of colour fidelity. The repetitive nature of the operation deterred one candidate. 'The mere fact of having to do 300 copies of one plate seemed to be her chief objection'.[5] The recruitment of suitable people was made even more difficult by the War which also delayed the Magazine's production. The publication of the last volume Sir Arthur edited – vol. 163 – had to be spread over two years when stocks of part II were destroyed during an air-raid.

Sir Arthur Hill made very few contributions himself, preferring to rely on the Kew staff and other experts. He maintained the close relationship with Edinburgh which Stapf had re-established, dedicating a volume to its Director, Sir William Wright Smith, who provided all the determinations for the primulas in the Magazine. In 1935 (plate 9382) floral dissections were removed from the plate itself and given as a line-drawing in the text. Stella Ross-Craig was now sharing the responsibility for illustrating the Magazine with Lilian Snelling.

Sir Arthur died as a result of a riding accident in 1941 and the Keeper of the Kew Herbarium, A. D. Cotton, stepped into the breach during the difficult days of the War. The evacuation of books and herbarium specimens from Kew prevented any exhaustive taxonomic research on the Magazine's descriptions. The ill-health of Miss Snelling but, more especially, the dearth of colourists delayed the publication of vol. 164 of which part 1 came out in 1943 and the final part in 1948. Cotton lamented that colourists 'appear to have become almost extinct.' The survival of the Magazine depended on adopting a modern illustration process. 'But for a very small circulation such as 250 the use of any process method is exceedingly costly. Our only hope seems to lie in the possibility of being able to devise a plan for selling some of the extra plates produced'.[6] In

---

[4] Royal Botanic Gardens, Kew. Library (Archives). IRHS/16, July 24, 1937.
[5] *Ibid*, H. R. Williams of Bernard Quaritch to Sir Arthur Hill, September 3, 1941.
[6] *Ibid*, A. D. Cotton, *Botanical Magazine*, Progress Report, October 12, 1945–January 7, 1946.

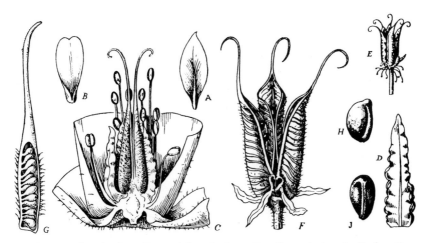

A, a sepal, nat. size ; B, a petal, nat. size ; C, a flower in longitudinal section, the upper portions of the sepals and petals cut off, × 4 ; D, a staminode, × 6 ; E, fruit, nat. size ; F, the same with two follicles removed, showing three seeds, × 3 ; G, a carpel, the ovary in longitudinal section, × 6 ; H, a seed in side view, × 16 ; J, a seed in dorsal view, × 16.

Semiaquilegia ecalcarata (plate 9382). First floral dissection in the
Botanical Magazine to be shown separately from the plate.

July 1947 the Botanical Magazine Committee considered estimates for three different illustration processes: four-colour half-tone, photolithography and collotype, and favoured the last one. Six months later they were not so certain and their preference was now for half-tone. In the event four-colour half-tone was chosen for vol. 165 (1948) and thus came to an end an unrivalled tradition of hand-colouring that had lasted for 160 years. During that time the quality of the colouring had varied from superior work where the colours were carefully blended to crude colour washes. A comparison of several copies will sometimes reveal slight variations in the colouring of the same plate. Certain colours – white and brown – were chemically unstable and have darkened with time but this can fortunately be remedied. For artistic as well as for economic reasons, the abandonment of hand-colouring was inevitable.

The introduction of half-tone plates also marked the beginning of yet another new series of the Magazine; the plate numbers recommenced at one but the original sequence of volume numbers was retained. The price of individual issues was raised to 21s. or £4 annually. W. B. Turrill, Keeper of the Herbarium and Library, became editor. With the formation of a cytological department in the Society's gardens at Wisley, the addition of chromosome numbers, whenever possible, was promised. The Botanical Magazine Committee decided that more plants of interest to the average gardener and available through nurseries should be selected. The decision of the Committee to change from the half-tone process to photogravure with vol. 166 was probably welcomed by those subscribers who disliked the shiny art paper on which the half-tone plates had been printed.

PLATE 39

Stained-glass window commemorating William Curtis by John Hayward in
St Mary's Church, Battersea. The design incorporates flowers from the
Flora Londinensis, the arms of the Society of Apothecaries and the Linnean Society
and a schematic map of the south bank of the Thames.

New vignette of Palm House at Kew used from vol. 169 (1952–53).

Within a few years photogravure was replaced by photolithography which has been employed to the present day.

In October 1951 it was announced that the production of future volumes would be spread over two years, that is only two numbers would be published in a year. This took effect from vol. 169 (1952–53) which had a redesigned cover by Ruari McLean for the new printers, Westerham Press; a new vignette of the Palm House was drawn by the wood-engraver, Joan Hassall. The long, rather rambling title was shortened to 'Curtis's Botanical Magazine containing coloured figures with descriptions and observations on the botany, history and culture of choice plants'.

In 1935 F. J. Chittenden started compiling a new cumulative index to the Magazine; with the assistance of botanists the nomenclature was revised and obsolescent names replaced by their modern equivalents.[7]

W. B. Turrill's editorship ceased with his death in December 1961. Lilian Snelling had retired in 1952 and the dedication in vol. 169 extolled her 'remarkable delicacy of accurate outlines, brilliancy of colour and intricate gradation of tone'. Stella Ross-Craig was joined by Ann Webster and Margaret Stones as regular artists. Following a directive from the Botanical Magazine Committee in 1949, Turrill had some of the plants figured in previous volumes redrawn. More accurate portraits of *Colquhounia coccinea* (N.S. plate 115), *Gentiana ascepiades* (N.S. plate 191), *Veltheimia capensis* (N.S. plate 215), and *Greyia sutherlandii* (N.S. plate 374), for example, replaced earlier plates.

It is always a matter of some surprise that well-known plants, long-standing friends of all gardeners, somehow got overlooked. Their omission might perhaps be due to the fact that they had already been adequately illustrated elsewhere.

---

[7] F. J. Chittenden, *Curtis's Botanical Magazine index. With a revision of the names of the plants depicted from the beginning in 1787 to the end of 1947, vol. 1 to vol. 164; to which is appended a brief history of the magazine . . . and an appendix giving the titles and numbers of the plates from vol. 165 to vol. 170,* 1956.

Turrill inserted the common wild daffodil, *Narcissus pseudo-narcissus* (N.S. plate 216), *Daphne mezereum* (N.S. plate 272), *Choisya ternata* (N.S. plate 318) and *Genista sagittalis* (N.S. plate 332).

Editors of the Magazine had always justified the exclusion of hybrids – not always rigorously observed – on the grounds that distinct species must take precedence. Recognizing that garden varieties were often superior to their parent species, the Botanical Magazine Committee decided that some first generation hybrids, of known parentage, should be included, provided they possessed noteworthy horticultural merit. Turrill himself described many of the hybrids selected.

Sir George Taylor, the Director at Kew, assumed the editorship after Turrill's death; he was successful in obtaining financial assistance for the Magazine from the Bentham–Moxon Trustees; in 1966 the Trustees helped with artists' fees, and four years later contributed to publication costs pending the outcome of discussions about long-term plans. Following negotiations with the Royal Horticultural Society in 1970, the copyright was assigned to the Bentham–Moxon Trust on January 1, 1971. Vol. 178 (1970–72) appeared under the imprint of the Bentham–Moxon Trust with support from the Stanley Smith Horticultural Trust. The Curwen Press which had printed parts 3 and 4 of vol. 177, now superseded the Westerham Press as printers. David R. Hunt, a Kew botanist, who had been appointed assistant editor, assumed full responsibility with vol. 179. The first Kew calender in 1974, compiled from a selection of Magazine plates, was a great success. With part 3 of vol. 180 the Academic Press took on publicity and sales. The entire remaining stock of vols. 71–164 (1845–1945) was sold to the natural history booksellers, Wheldon and Wesley. In 1980 Curwen Books replaced the Academic Press as distributor. Christopher Grey-Wilson edited vol. 184 (1982–83), the last to proclaim *Curtis's Botanical Magazine* as its title.

There was little change in policy or style in the final years of the *Botanical Magazine* under the editorship of Sir George Taylor, David Hunt and Christopher Grey-Wilson. Margaret Stones, the principal artist for many of the volumes of the New Series, now shared the responsibility with Ann Farrer, Mary Grierson, Christabel King and Pandora Sellars, all newcomers whose sensitive yet confident plant portraits upheld the traditional skills of the botanical artist. It was a joy to see some of the very early work of Lilian Snelling: *Ligustrum compactum* var. *velutinum* (N.S. plate 759), for instance, which she had painted nearly half a century before. The dedication in vol. 182 to Stella Ross-Craig and her husband, J. Robert Sealy, commemorated a long association with the Magazine that had begun under Otto Stapf. *Corylopsis sinensis* (*willmottiae*) (N.S. plate 438), *Eucalyptus pulveralenta* (N.S. plate 525), *Syzygium paniculatum* (N.S. plate 529) and *Idesia polycarpa* (N.S. plate 649) superseded earlier plates which had been considered either poorly drawn or lacking some essential characters.

The hunt for more astonishing omissions yielded *Magnolia virginiana* (N.S. plate 457), *Physocarpus opulifolius* (N.S. plate 459), *Maurandya barclaiana* (N.S. plate 810) and *Helianthus annuus* (N.S. plate 755). The white-flowered variety of

Ranunculus asiaticus had been described in 1934 and the single yellow variety was figured in 1977 (N. S. plate 741). In 1597 John Gerard described a double red variety of this common plant of the eastern Mediterranean 'from whence there hath been brought plants at divers times, and by divers persons, but they have perished by reason of the long journey, want of skill of the bringers, that have suffered them to be in a boxe or suchlike so long, that when we received them, they have been as drie as ginger'.[8] In the seventeenth century many double and single varieties were being successfully bred by florists and by the beginning of Victoria's reign there were about 1,000 named varieties. But fickle fashion and, more especially, the labour-intensive attention they demand has led to their decline in popularity.

The acquisition in 1965 by Kew of Wakehurst Place some 64 km (40 mi) away in Sussex with its outstanding collection of trees and shrubs carefully selected by Gerald Loder, Lord Wakehurst, provided the *Botanical Magazine* with an abundant choice of new plants. From Lord Wakehurst's Australasian introductions were selected three olearias and a *Correa*; from China *Gaultheria*, *Rehderodendron* and *Persea*; a berberis and a skimmia from the Himalayas; and one of H. F. Comber's escallonias from South America.

In 1945 a solitary specimen of the beautiful climber, *Tecomanthe speciosa* (N.S. plate 618) was discovered on Great Island in the Three Kings Islands off the New Zealand coast. Deforestation by the Maoris and then the voracious appetite of goats which had been deliberately introduced as a source of food for shipwrecked sailors, had almost eliminated it. All the goats were slaughtered in an attempt to save a plant which had such a tenuous hold in the wild. Fortunately it thrives in cultivation; the Magazine plate was drawn from a healthy plant at Sunte House in Sussex.

The botanical excursions of Admiral Furse and his wife in the 1960s in Iran, Afghanistan and Central Asia gave the Magazine five irises besides much else. A revival of interest in begonias, neglected for more than 50 years, prompted the inclusion of *B. saxicola* (N.S. plate 739) from Brazil and *B. serratipetala* from the Papua New Guinea. David Hunt's personal interest in the flora of Mexico where he made several field trips doubtless accounts for more than 20 plants from that country being figured. Orchids staged a spectacular come-back under Christopher Grey-Wilson; three *Paphiopedilum*, a *Miltonia*, *Dendrobium*, *Pecteilis* and the whole of part 3 of vol. 184 was devoted to *Pleione*, the popular 'window-sill orchid'. Although a monographic treatment had been considered by previous editors, this was the first time it had actually been attempted. The normal quantity was doubled for this particular number and it completely sold out.

The flora of the Sino-Himalayas was still a pervasive presence in the Magazine. Frank Ludlow and George Sherriff found new species of rhododendrons and primulas in Bhutan and Tibet but many of the primulas seldom set seed in the British climate. *Metasequoia glyptostroboides* (N.S. plate 716) had only been known from fossil records until a solitary specimen of this redwood was found in 1941 in northeastern Sichuan where villagers worshipped it as a sacred tree. In 1948 the Arnold Arboretum collected seed, freely distributed it, and it

[8] J. Gerard, *Herball*, 1597, p. 813.

The
KEW MAGAZINE
Vol 1 Part 1 April 1984

Incorporating
CURTIS'S
Botanical Magazine
Royal Botanic Gardens, Kew in association with Collingridge

ISSN 0265-3842

Cover of the first number of the *Kew Magazine*, April 1984.

proved so adaptable to different climates and soils that it is now as common as that other 'living fossil', *Ginkgo biloba*. Bearing in mind the revolution wrought in the composition of British gardens by Chinese plants, it was appropriate that the last plate to be published in *Curtis's Botanical Magazine* should be an introduction by E. H. Wilson, *Castanea henryi* (N.S. plate 882).

There have always been critics who have complained, not without some justification, that the *Botanical Magazine* was written by botanists for botanists. If the Magazine were to survive it had to appeal to a wider audience and this could only be achieved by enlarging the scope of its contents. After careful deliberation, tinged perhaps with some regret, a new departure was made with the first number of the *Kew Magazine, incorporating Curtis's Botanical Magazine* in April 1984, published by Kew in association with Collingridge. Subscribers are being sought amongst botanists, gardeners, ecologists, conservationists and admirers of botanical art. The artistic tradition of the *Botanical Magazine* is being perpetuated in every quarterly issue by specially commissioned plant portraits, reproducing by photolithography the work of modern botanical artists. The editor, Christopher Grey-Wilson, encouraged perhaps by his earlier success with the number exclusively on one genus (*Pleione* in vol. 184) has shown a preference for a similar selective treatment of other genera – *Arisaema, Echinocereus* and *Dendrobium.* Much more comprehensive will be the new series of *Kew Magazine Monographs* which will examine the taxonomy and cultivation of specific genera, incorporating illustrations from *Curtis's Botanical Magazine* and the *Kew Magazine. Echinocereus* was published in 1985; *Cyclamen, Paphiopedilum, Lewisia* and others are in preparation. 'Plants in peril' is a regular feature, significant developments at Kew and elsewhere in the botanical and horticultural world are briefly reported, book reviews are given, and the reader, for the first time, has an opportunity to express his opinion in a correspondence column. This offspring of *Curtis's Botanical Magazine* is a healthy, confident youngster which promises to be a credit to its distinguished parent. We wish it a long and prosperous life.

APPENDIX

Artists, engravers and lithographers in
'Curtis's Botanical Magazine'

Where contributions are few in number, all the plate numbers are cited. In the case of prolific artists like Sydenham Edwards, Sir William Hooker, W. H. Fitch, Matilda Smith, Lilian Snelling, etc., only the first and last plates they drew are given. Since many plates are unsigned, the actual contributions of individual artists may be greater than indicated in the following list.

(N.S. = New Series)

(*fl.* = flourished)

ADAM, Robert Moyes (1885–1967)
Gardener, Royal Botanic Garden,
Edinburgh, 1903. Photographer and artist.
Assistant in the Studio, 1915–49. Artist to
Botanical Society of Edinburgh.
pl. 9030 (1924)

ADAMS, Miss (*fl.* 1830s)
Daughter of Capt Adams, Witham, Essex.
Friend of Samuel Curtis and drew plants in
his garden at Glazenwood.
pls. 3475, 3490, 3523 (1836)

ALLEN, John (*fl.* 1890s)
pl. 7279 (1893)

ATKINSON, Gerald (1893–1971)
Studied at Hull College of Art. Botanical
artist and photographer, Kew Gardens,
1922–59. Contributed drawings to Hooker's
Icones plantarum.
pls. 8950, 8976, 8985, 8992, 9007, 9010,
9012, 9017, 9019, 9027, 9029, 9038, 9043,
9061, 9067, 9077, 9082, 9108, 9114–15,
9119, 9124, 9172, 9178, 9184, 9194, 9212,
9216–22, 9225, 9302, 9379, N.S. 82
(1923–49)

BAGGS, B. M. (*fl.* 1930s)
Acquaintance of E. A. Bowles?
pls. 8877, 8894 (1938)

BANCROFT, Edward Nathaniel (1772–1842)
Physician to forces in Jamaica from 1811.
Contributed to J. Lunan, *Hortus Jamaicensis*,
1814.
pl. 3059 (1831)

BARBER, Mary Elizabeth (*née* Bowker)
(1818–1899)
To South Africa in 1820. Correspondent of
Darwin, the Hookers and W. H. Harvey.
Collected plants and insects.
pl. 5607 (1866)

BARNARD, Anne (*née* Henslow) (*d.* 1899)
Daughter of Prof. John Stevens Henslow. Sir
Joseph Hooker's sister-in-law. Illustrated
D. Oliver, *Lessons in elementary botany*, 1864.
pls. 6404–7341 (1879–94) – 115 plates

BARTHOLOMEW, Valentine (1799–1879)
Associate of Society of Painters in
Watercolours, 1835. Flower Painter in
Ordinary to the Queen.
pl. 3479 (1836)

BATES, E. (*fl.* 1880s)
Lithographer.
pls. 7044–47, 7051–57, 7061–67, 7074–77,
7098–7100 (1889–90)

BAUER, Francis Andreas (1758–1840)
Botanical artist, Kew Gardens, 1790–1840.
Noted for his skill with the microscope.
Illustrated: *Delineations of exotick plants
cultivated in royal garden at Kew*, 1796–1803;
Strelitzia depicta, 1818; J. Lindley, *Illustrations
of Orchidaceous plants*, 1830–38.
pls. 3172, 3377–78, (1832–35); *Companion to
Botanical Magazine*, 1837, pl. 32

BEWICKE, Mrs (*fl.* 1820s)
Close House near Newcastle,
Northumberland.
pl. 2744 (1827)

BOJER, Wenceslaus (1795–1856)
Born in Bohemia. To Mauritius in 1820.
Curator, Mauritius Museum. Prof. of
Botany, Royal College, Port Louis, 1828.
Director, Royal Botanic Garden,
Pamplemousses. Collected plants in
Mauritius, Madagascar and Zanzibar,
1820–35.
pls. 2884, 2970–71, 2976, 3144, 3325–26
(1829–34)

BOOTH, William Beattie (c. 1804–1874)
Gardener, Horticultural Society of London,
Chiswick, 1824–30. Gardener to Sir C.
Lemon at Carclew, Cornwall. Assistant
Secretary, Horticultural Society, 1858–59.
Illustrations and descriptions of . . . Camellieae,
1831.
pl. 3677 (1839)

BROOKS, Vincent (later Vincent Brooks,
Day and Son)
Lithographers.
pls. 4782 (1854) to end of 1920

BROWN, Nicholas Edward (1849–1934)
Curator, W. W. Saunder's Museum,
Reigate. Assistant, Kew Herbarium, 1873;
Assistant Keeper, 1909–14. Authority on
South African plants.
pls. 6375, 6379 (1878)

BURBIDGE, Frederick William Thomas
(1847–1905)
Gardener, Kew Gardens, 1868–70. Collected
plants in Borneo for James Veitch and Sons,
1877–78. Curator, Trinity College, Dublin,
1879–1905. *Art of botanical drawing*, 1873;
Narcissus, 1875; *Gardens of the Sun*, 1880, etc.
pls. 6403, 6489 (1879–80)

COLE, Lady Frances (*fl.* 1830s)
Wife of Gen. Sir Galbraith Lowry Cole,
successively Governor of Mauritius and Cape
of Good Hope.
pl. 2869 (1830)

CUNNINGHAM, Allan (1791–1839)
Employed at Kew Gardens. Collected plants
for Kew in Brazil, Australia and New
Zealand, 1814–31. Superintendent, Botanic
Gardens, Sydney, 1836–38.
pl. 3184 (1832)

CURTIS, Caroline (1805–1890)
Daughter of Samuel Curtis (1779–1860).
pls. 2628, 2667, 2672–73, 2675, 2682, 2784
(1826–27)

CURTIS, Charles M. (*c.* 1795–1839)
Brother of John Curtis (1791–1862).
Contributed plates to N. Wallich, *Plantae
Asiaticae rariores*, 1830–32; J. F. Royle,
*Illustrations of botany . . . of Himalayan
Mountains*, 1839; J. Stephenson, *Medical
botany*, 1827–31; R. Brown, *Miscellaneous
botanical works*, 1866–68.
pls. 2611–12, 2617, 2619–20, 2676, 2739,
2816, 3316 (1826–34)

CURTIS, Georgiana (1823–1906)
Daughter of Samuel Curtis (1779–1860).
pl. 3928 (1842)

CURTIS, Henry (1820–1889)
Son of Samuel Curtis (1779–1860).
pl. 3411 (1835)

CURTIS, John (1791–1862)
Entomologist and artist. *British entomology*,
1824–39.
pls. 2083–3150 (1819–32) – over 400 plates.

CURTIS, Sarah Maria (1802–1872)
Daughter of Samuel Curtis (1779–1860).
pls. 3412, 3483 (1835–36)

CURTIS, William (*b.* 1804)
Son of Samuel Curtis (1779–1860).
pls. 3333, 3352, 3415, 3530 (1834–36)

DALLY, Miss (*fl.* 1840s)
Drew plants at Samuel Curtis's garden at
Glazenwood.
pls. 3801, 3808 (1840)

DARNELL, A. W. (*fl.* 1920s)
Lithographer.
pls. 8996, 8998–9011, 9013–15, 9017–23,
9060 (1924–25)

DARTON, W. and Co. (*fl.* 1790s)
Engraver.
pls. 129–32 (1790)

DUNCOMBE, E. (*fl.* 1810s–20s)
pls. 2102, 2660, 2677–78, 2680–81 (1819–26)

DURHAM, Miss E. (*fl.* 1840s)
pl. 3909 (1841)

EDWARDS, Sydenham Teast (1768–1819)
Trained as an artist by William Curtis and
became principal artist for *Botanical Magazine*
until he resigned to found *Botanical Register* in
1815. Illustrated: R. W. Dickson, *Complete
dictionary of practical gardening*, 1805–07;
W. Curtis, *Lectures on Botany*, 1805.
pls. 2 (1787) to vol. 42 (1815) are mainly by
Edwards. Many of the succeeding anonymous
plates are almost certainly by Edwards.
After his death the *Botanical Magazine*
published his earlier drawings: 2151, 2157,
2159–60, 2187, 2195, 2209, 2218, 2220,
2233, 2286, 2316, 2321, 2325, 2329, 2346,
2388–89, 2439, 2679, 3153 (1832)

ELLIS, Mrs (*fl.* 1850s)
Wife of Rev. William Ellis (1794–1872),
missionary in Madagascar, 1853–65.
pls. 5094, 5179 (1859–60)

FARRER, Ann (*b.* 1950)
Grand-daughter of Reginald Farrer.
Illustrated: *Collins guide to grasses, sedges and
rushes*; O. Polunin and A. Stainton, *Flowers of
the Himalayas* and *The Plantsman*.
pl. N.S. 810 (1980)

FITCH, John Nugent (1840–1927)
Nephew of W. H. Fitch (1817–1892) who
trained him as a botanical artist and
lithographer. Illustrated: *Floral Magazine*,
1878–81; R. Warner and B. S. Williams,
Orchid album, 1882–97. He had lithographed
about 2,500 plates for the *Botanical Magazine*
before he lost the use of his fingers.
pls. 6342 (1878) to vol. 146 (1920)

FITCH, Walter Hood (1817–1892)
Botanical artist at Kew Gardens, 1841. Drew
over 2,700 plates for *Botanical Magazine* and
about 500 for Hooker's *Icones Plantarum*,
1836–76. Over 10,000 of his drawings were
published (see *Kew Bulletin*, 1915, pp. 277–84
for complete list). Author of eight articles on
'Botanical drawing' in *Gardeners' Chronicle*,
1869.
pls. 3353–6389 (1834–78)

GLOVER, Thomas (*fl.* 1830s)
Manchester.
pl. 3295 (1834)

GORDON, Victoria
pls. N.S. 698, 735, 740, 745, (1974–77)

GREVILLE, Robert Kaye (1794–1866)
Excelled in rendering microscopic detail in
pencil. In later years earned his living as a
landscape painter of the Scottish Highlands.
Scottish Cryptogamic flora, 1823–28; *Icones
Filicum*, 1827–31 (joint author with W. J.
Hooker).
pls. 2507, 2615, 2658, 2811, 2926, 2952,
2965–66, 2996, 3040, 3044, 3067, 3136,
3142, 3287, 3309 (1824–34)

GRIERSON, Mary (*b.* 1912)
Botanical artist, Kew Gardens, 1960.
Illustrated P. F. Hunt, *Orchidaceae*, 1973 and
Country Life Book of Orchids, 1978.
pls. N.S. 444, 448, 451, 453, 461, 468–72,
474, 477, 483, 512, 580, 593, 620, 664, 668,
699–700, 758, (1964–78); *Kew Magazine*, pl.
63 (1986)

GUILDING, Rev. Lansdown (1797–1831)
Colonial chaplain, St Vincent. *Account of
Botanical Garden in Island of St Vincent*, 1825.
pls. 2741–42, 2749–50, 2756A, 2757B,
2833–34, 2869–71, 2911–12, 3095, 3111–12,
3130, 3132, 3139, 3157–59 (1827–32)

HARRISON, Mary (*née* Rossiter)
(1788–1875)
Married Richard Harrison who received
orchids from Henry and William Harrison in
Brazil. Exhibited at New Society of Painters
in Watercolours.
pls. 2820, 2878, 3109, 3116, 3151, 3154,
3173 (1828–32)

HARVEY, William Henry (1811–1866)
Professor of Botany, Royal Dublin Society,
1848; Trinity College, Dublin, 1856.
pl. 25 in *Companion to Botanical Magazine*,
1835–37

HENSLOW, Rev. John Stevens (1796–1861)
Professor of Botany, Cambridge, 1825–61.
pl. 3166 (1832)

HERBERT, Hon. and Rev. William
(1778–1847)
Rector, Spofforth, 1814–40. Dean of
Manchester, 1840–47. *Amaryllidaceae*, 1837.
pls. 2121–3873 (1820–41) – 62 plates

HIGGINS, Vera (*née* Cockburn) (1892–1968)
Scientific Officer, National Physical
Laboratory. Authority on succulent plants.
pl. N.S. 167 (1951)

HOLDEN, Mr (*fl.* 1850s)
Warrington.
pls. 5120, 5129 (1859)

HOLLAND, T. (*fl.* 1830s)
pl. 3380 (1835)

HOOKER, Sir William Jackson (1785–1865)
Professor of Botany, Glasgow, 1820.
Director, Kew Gardens, 1841–65.
pls. 2689–3795 (1826–40) – over 670 plates

HORSFALL, Mrs C. (*fl.* 1830s)
Wife of Charles Horsfall, who had a notable
collection of plants at Everton, Liverpool.
pls. 3076, 3229, 3315, 3430, 3499, 3534
(1831–36)

HUTH, (*fl.* 1930s)
Lithographer.
pls. 8874–75, 8889–90 (1938)

HYDE, Francis (*fl.* 1830s)
Late of 12th Lancers.
pls. 2963–64 (1830)

KELLET, A. (1920s)
Botanical artist, Kew Gardens, 1921.
pls. 8934, 8943, 8947, 8949, 8950–51,
8954–56, 8962, 8964, 8966, 8979, 9024, 9204
(1922–30)

KING, Christabel (*b.* 1950)
pls. N.S. 706–877 (1976–83) – 68 plates; *Kew
Magazine*, pls. 43–44, 48, 57–58, 60–61,
65–69 (1986); *Genus Echinocereus* (Kew
Magazine Monograph, 1985)

LANGHORNE, Joanna Asquith (*née* Lowe)
(*b.* 1945)
Botanical artist, Kew Gardens, 1973.
pls. N.S. 757, 803 (1978–80); *Kew Magazine*,
pls. 8, 10, 64 (1986)

LOWE, Rev. Richard Thomas (1802–1874)
Chaplain, Madeira, 1832–54.
pls. 3227, 3234 (1833)

MACFARLANE, J. L. (1836–*c*.1913)
Artist and lithographer who drew for
nurserymen. Contributed plates to *Florist*.
pl. 7576 (1898)

MCNAB, James (1810–1878)
Curator, Royal Botanic Garden, Edinburgh,
1849. Contributed plates to R. Sweet, *British
Flower Garden*, 1834–37.
pls. 2930, 2950–51, 2975, 3025, 3181, 3194,
3201–02, 3211, 3230, 3245, 3252, 3255–56,
3278, 3280, 3294, 3300, 3327–28, 3344,
3350, 3444, 3518, 3746, 3770, 3888 (1829–41)

MOGGRIDGE, John Traherne (1842–1874)
Contributions to Flora of Mentone, 1864–68.
pl. 6139 (1874)

MOSS, Miss (*fl.* 1830s)
Daughter of John Moss, an orchid collector
at Otterspool, near Liverpool?
pl. 3573 (1837)

MURRAY, Miss (*fl.* 1840s)
Daughter of S. Murray, Superintendent of
Glasgow Botanic Garden?
pl. 3999 (1843)

NICHOLSON, Thomas (1799–1877)
Ship's surgeon. In Antigua, 1819, 1822–27.
pls. 3071, 3098 (1831)

NORBURY, M. (*fl.* 1840s)
pl. 3819 (1840)

NORTON, Hon. Miss C. E. C. (*fl.* 1830s)
pls. 3293, 3301 (1834)

NUTTALL, Thomas (1786–1859)
Curator, Botanic Garden, Harvard, 1822–34.
Returned to England in 1842. His nephew,
T. J. Booth, collected plants for him in
Assam and Bhutan.
pl. 3655 (1838)

ORMEROD, Eleanor A. (1828–1901)
Horticultural entomologist.
pls. 6387, 6461, 6486, 6556 (1878–81)

POPE, Clara Maria (*née* Leight) (*fl.*
1760s–1838)
Exhibited at Royal Academy. Painted
portraits and miniatures; gave drawing
lessons. Contributed plates to S. Curtis,
Beauties of Flora, 1806–20, and *Monograph on
the Genus Camellia*, 1819.
pls. 3375, 3644 (1835–38)

PORTER, Sir Robert Ker (1777–1842)
Consul-General at Caracas, Venezuela,
1826–41.
pls. 3723–24 (1839)

PRICE, Valerie (*b.* 1958)
Kew Magazine, pls. 45, 50–55, (1986)

PURVES, Mrs Rodella Anne (*b.* 1945)
Royal Botanic Garden, Edinburgh.
pls. N.S. 864, 866; *Kew Magazine*, pls. 1, 3
(1984)

RAY, Susie
Kew Magazine, pls. 27–28 (1985)

ROSS-CRAIG, Stella (*b.* 1906)
Drawings of British Plants, 1947–74; vol. 182
(1978–80) of *Botanical Magazine* dedicated to
her and her husband, J. R. Sealy.
pls. 8919–9688 (1932–48) – 113 plates; N.S.
4–791 (1948–80) – 220 plates

RUDGE, Mrs Anne (*fl.* 1820s)
Drew plates for *Plantarum Guianae rariorum*,
1805, written by her husband, Edward
Rudge.
pl. 2465 (1824)

SANSOM, Francis (*fl.* 1780s–1810s)
Engraver. In partnership with William
Bawtree until 1784. In Rotterdam, 1788–90.
Engraved plates in W. Curtis, *Flora
Londinensis*, and *Lectures on botany*, 1805; R.
W. Dickson, *Complete dictionary of practical
gardening*, 1805–07.
Drew and engraved pls. 191, 193–98;
engraved all subsequent plates to pl. 1735
(1792–1815)

SAUNDERS, William Wilson (1809–1879)
Treasurer, Linnean Society, 1861–73.
Secretary, Royal Horticultural Society,
1863–66. Had garden at Hillfield, Reigate.
pls. 5873, 5946, 6377, 6380 (1870–78)

SCHOENFELD, J. (*fl.* 1860s)
pl. 5382 (1863)

SCOTT, John (*fl.* 1830s)
Physician in Tasmania.
pls. 3145, 3187 (1832)

SELLARS, Pandora (*b.* 1936)
pls. N.S. 820, 833, 838, 849, 851, 855, 872,
880 (1981–83); *Kew Magazine*, pls. 7, 9,
11–12, 25, 30, 38–42, 46–47, 56, 59, 70–72
(1986)

SHORT, Charles Wilkins (1794–1863)
Physician of Louisville, Kentucky. His
collection of American and exotic plants was
given to Academy of Natural Sciences,
Philadelphia.
pls. 3232, 3342, 3496 (1833–36); *Companion to
Botanical Magazine*, 1835–37, pl. 20

SMITH, Mrs E. J. (*fl.* 1870s)
Of Coalport, Shropshire.
pl. 6129 (1874)

SMITH, Matilda (1854–1926)
Trained by Sir Joseph Hooker and was
principal artist for *Botanical Magazine*,
1878–1922. Contributed plates to *Transactions
of Linnean Society*; Hooker's *Icones Plantarum*;
W. Botting Hemsley, *Report on . . . voyage of
H.M.S. Challenger*; *Botany*, 1885; I. B. Balfour,
Botany of Socotra, 1888.
pls. 6386–8948 (1878–1923) – over 2,300
plates

SMITH, Worthington George (1835–1917)
Botanical artist and mycologist. Drew for
Gardeners' Chronicle, 1869–1910, and *Floral
Magazine*.
pls. 6376, 6378 (1878)

SNELLING, Lilian (1879–1972)
Artist and lithographer. Trained by H. J.
Elwes. Artist at Botanic Garden, Edinburgh,
1916–21. Contributed plates to *Supplement to
Elwes' Monograph of Genus Lilium*, 1934–40; F.
Stoker, *Book of lilies*, 1943; F. C. Stern, *Study
of Genus Paeonia*, 1946.
pls. 8876–9686; N.S. 1–759 (1923–80) – over
740 plates

SOWERBY, James (1757–1822)
Botanical artist. Studied at Royal Academy.
*Botanical drawing book or an easy introduction to
drawing flowers according to nature*, 1788. Drew
2,592 plants for his *English Botany*,
1790–1814. Contributed plates to W. Curtis,
Flora Londinensis; J. E. Smith, *Exotic Botany*,
1804–05; W. Woodville, *Medical botany*,
1790–94.
pls. 1, 4, 10–12, 14, 16–17, 19, 20–21, 24,
26, 28, 32–33, 37, 42, 44, 47, 49–52, 54–56,
58, 61, 67, 70, 72, 76, 79–80, 85, 87–109,
111, 113, 115–18, 121 (these are based on a
list issued to subscribers in 1809), 2292,
2305, 2310, 2328, 2354, 2683 (1787–1826)

SOWERBY, James de Carle (1787–1871)
Son of James Sowerby. With his brother,
C. E. Sowerby, produced *Supplement to
English Botany*, 1831–40.
pls. 3078–80, 3297, 3339 (1831–34)

SOWERBY
Could be J. de C. or J. E.
pls. 5091–92 (1859)

SPANOGUE
Companion to the *Botanical Magazine*,
1835–37.
pl. 17.

STAPF, Otto (1857–1933)
Keeper, Kew Herbarium, 1909–22.
pls. 9117, 9125, 9315 (1927–33)

STONES, E. Margaret (*b.*1920)
Australian botanical artist. Contributed
plates to W. Curtis, *Endemic flora of Australia*,
1967–78.
pls. N.S. 309–882 (1958–1983); *Kew
Magazine*, pl. 4 – over 400 plates

SWAN, Joseph (*fl.* 1820s–1840s)
Engraver, Glasgow. Engraved plates in
botanical works by W. J. Hooker and R. K.
Greville.
pls. 2689–4173 (1826–45); *Companion to
Botanical Magazine*, 1835–37, pls. 2, 4–29

SYME, P. (*fl.* 1820s)
pls. 2204, 2238, 2461 (1821–23)

TELFAIR, Annabella (*née* Chamberlain)
(*d.*1832)
Wife of Charles Telfair, surgeon and
Supervisor of Botanic Garden, Mauritius,
1826–29.
pls. 2817, 2891, 2902, 2970–71 (1828–30)

THISELTON-DYER, Lady Harriet Ann (*née*
Hooker) (1854–1945)
Daughter of Sir Joseph Hooker and wife of
Sir William Thiselton-Dyer. Received tuition
in botanical drawing from W. H. Fitch.
Contributed drawings to J. B. Balfour,
Botany of Socotra, 1888.
pls. 6348–7666 (1878–99) – 84 plates

TREVITHICK, William Edward (1900–1958)
Kew gardener, 1920. Assistant, Kew
Herbarium, 1923. Contributed drawings to

Flora of West Tropical Africa, 1927–29; J.
Hutchinson, *Families of flowering plants*,
1926–34.
pls. 9030–9643 (1924–42) – 73 plates: some
drawn in conjunction with other artists;
some he only lithographed

VANDERGUCHT, S. (*fl.* 1840s)
Employee of Belgian nurseryman, Van
Houtte of Ghent.
pl. 4012 (1843)

WEBSTER Ann V. (*b.*1930)
pls. N.S. 168–566 (1951–70) – 103 plates

WEDDELL, Messrs (*fl.* 1810s–1820s)
Walworth, London. The firm engraved and
lithographed many botanical books.
Lithographed plates in *Botanical Magazine*,
1815–26. H. Weddell drew pl. 1734 (1815)

WITHERS, Augusta Innes (*née* Baker)
(*c.*1793–1860s)
Exhibited at Society of British Artists.
Painter of Flowers to Queen Adelaide, 1830.
Flower and Fruit Painter in Ordinary to
Queen Victoria, 1864. Contributed to
J. Bateman, *Orchidaceae of Mexico and
Guatemala*, 1837–43; *Pomological Magazine*;
Maund's *Botanist*.
pls. 3629, 3631, 3638, 3656, 3706, 3767
(1838–39)

WOOLWARD, Miss P. H. (*fl.* 1870s)
pl. 6388 (1878)

WRAY, Martha (*c.*1775–1864)
Cultivated exotic plants at Oakfield,
Cheltenham. Vol. 67 (1840–41) of *Botanical
Magazine* dedicated to her.
pls. 3875–76 (1841)

WILSON, William (1799–1871)
Solicitor and bryologist.
pl. 9 in *Companion to Botanical Magazine*,
1835–37.

WRIGLEY, Mrs E. G. (*fl.* 1870s)
Of Bury, Lancashire.
pl. 6144 (1875)

YOUNG, Miss M. (*fl.* 1830s)
Friend of Rev. R. T. Lowe.
pls. 3293, 3296, 3303, 3305, 3356, 3360,
3366, 3390, 3408 (1834–35)

BIBLIOGRAPHY

Obituary of William Curtis, *Gentleman's Magazine*, July 1799, pp. 628–29; August 1799, pp. 635–39 by 'Kewensis', probably S. Goodenough.

Thornton, R. J., 'Sketch of the life and writings of the late Mr William Curtis' (W. Curtis, *Lectures on Botany*, vol. 3, 1805, pp. 1–33).

Smith, Sir James E., 'William Curtis' (A. Rees, *Cyclopaedia*, vol. 10, 1819).

Curtis, S., 'Memoirs of the life and writings of the late Mr William Curtis' (*General indexes to the plants contained in the first fifty-three volumes of the Botanical Magazine*, 1828, pp. v–xxxii).

Botting Hemsley, W., 'The history of the Botanical Magazine 1787–1904' (*A new and complete index to the Botanical Magazine . . . to which is prefixed a history of the Magazine*, 1906, pp. v–lxiii (this history is a consolidation of articles from the *Gardeners' Chronicle*, 1887)).

Stapf, O., 'The Botanical Magazine: its history and mission' (*Journal of the Royal Horticultural Society*, vol. 51, 1926, pp. 29–43).

Curtis, W. H., *William Curtis 1746–1799*, 1941.

Lousley, J. E., 'William Curtis (1746–1799)' (*London Naturalist*, no. 25, 1945, pp. 3–12); (*Journal of the Royal Horticultural Society*, vol. 71, 1946, pp. 98–100, 124–29).

Curtis Museum, Alton, Hampshire. *Catalogue of exhibition in commemoration of the bicentenary of the birth of William Curtis*, 1946.

Blunt, W., 'The Botanical Magazine' (*The art of botanical illustration*, 1950, pp. 184–88).

Synge, P. M., 'The Botanical Magazine' (*Journal of the Royal Horticultural Society*, vol. 73, 1948, pp. 5–11).

Turrill, W. B., 'Curtis's Botanical Magazine' (*Proceedings of the Seventh International Botanical Congress, Stockholm 1950*, 1953, pp. 83–87).

Chittenden, F. J., 'History of Curtis's Botanical Magazine' (*Curtis's Botanical Magazine index . . . volume 1 to volume 164*, 1956, pp. 251–69).

ACKNOWLEDGEMENTS

I am grateful for the help and facilities of the Royal Botanic
Gardens at Kew, the Hampshire County Museum, the Curtis Museum
at Alton, the Hunt Institute for Botanical Documentation, the
Linnean Society, and the Royal Horticultural Society. I would also
like to acknowledge the interest and assistance of Mr Howard Swann,
Dr Christopher Grey-Wilson and Nigel P. Taylor.

The illustrations are from the resources of the Library of
the Royal Botanic Gardens, Kew, with the exception of the
following which are reproduced by courtesy of their owners:

Frontispiece: Royal Horticultural Society
Plates 1 and 2: Mrs S. Jackson
Plates 3 and 5: Fitzwilliam Museum, Cambridge,
Plate 39: John Hayward.

Black and white illustrations
page 10: British Museum,
pages 20 and 29: Hunt Institute for Botanical Documentation,
pages 25, 85 and 174 (left): Linnean Society.

INDEX